PHILOSOPHY OF SCIENCE TODAY

PHILOSOPHY OF SCIENCE TODAY

Edited by SIDNEY MORGENBESSER

BASIC BOOKS, Inc., Publishers
New York   *London*

The Authors

MORTON BECKNER, Professor of Philosophy at Pomona College, California, received his doctorate at Columbia University. He has taught at Brooklyn College and Santa Barbara and at Pomona College, Claremont, California, since 1957.

MAX BLACK, Professor of Philosophy at Cornell University, has both a Ph.D. and a D.Lit. from London University. Dr. Black has been visiting professor at Columbia, Harvard, and Kyoto (Japan) universities and at the University of Washington. He is a past president of the American Philosophical Association (Eastern division) and holds membership in the Institut International de Philosophie. He has been granted a Guggenheim fellowship and a research grant by the National Science Foundation. His publications are numerous and widely known. He is the author of *Models and Metaphors* and *Companion to Wittgenstein's Tractatus* and editor of *Philosophy in America*.

PAUL FEYERABEND, Professor of Philosophy at the University of California (Berkeley), earned his doctorate at the University of Vienna. He has taught at the Vienna Institute for the Sciences and Fine Arts; he was a fellow at the Minnesota Center for the Philosophy of Science; and he was co-chairman of the Seminar of Modern Physics at the European Forum Alpbach (Austria). He was the recipient, in 1954, of the Austrian president's prize for achievement in the sciences and fine arts. His numerous writings are in the field of the quantum theory and the theory of knowledge.

NELSON GOODMAN is the Harry Austryn Wolfson Professor of Philosophy at Brandeis University. He received his Ph.D. from Harvard in 1941. He was a Guggenheim Fellow in 1946 and is a Fellow of the American Academy of Arts and Sciences. He has taught or given special lecture series at Harvard, Princeton, Oxford, and London universities. He is associated with research being conducted at the Harvard Center for Cognitive Studies and the Harvard Graduate School of Education and is the author of numerous articles and of two books, *Structure of Appearance* and *Fact, Fiction and Forecast*.

ADOLF GRÜNBAUM, Director of the Center for Philosophy of Science and Andrew Mellon Professor of Philosophy at the University of Pittsburgh, received his doctorate from Yale in 1950. He is the author of *Philosophical Problems of Space and Time* and contributor to many books and journals. He has been a Faculty-Fellow of the Ford Foundation and was given four research grants by the National Science Foundation. He is the president of the Philosophy of Science Association.

NORWOOD RUSSELL HANSON, Professor of Philosophy at Yale University, holds doctorates from both Oxford and Cambridge universities. His research grants have been from Fulbright, the Institute of Advanced Study at Princeton, the Ford and Rockefeller Foundations, and the American Council of Learned Societies. During World War II he was a U.S. Marine Corps fighter pilot. He is the author of *Pattern of Discovery* and *The Concept of the Position*.

CARL G. HEMPEL, Stuart Professor of Philosophy at Princeton University, studied mathematics, physics, and philosophy at the universities of Goettingen, Heidelberg, Berlin (Ph.D. 1934), and Vienna. Since 1955 he has been at Princeton. He has also taught at Harvard and Columbia universities and served as a Fulbright Fellow at Oxford. He holds membership in the American Philosophical Association and the Association for Symbolic Logic and is a Fellow of the American Academy of Arts and Sciences. Dr. Hempel's teaching and research have been in the fields of logic, epistemology, and the methodology and philosophy of science. He is the author of *Aspects of Scientific Explanation*.

LEON HENKIN, Professor of Mathematics at the University of California, Berkeley, received an A.B. degree from Columbia University and M.A. and Ph.D. degrees from Princeton University. He was appointed Assistant Professor of Mathematics at the University of Southern California and joined the faculty of the University of California in 1953. Professor Henkin has been a Fulbright Research Scholar at the University of Amsterdam, visiting professor at Dartmouth College, and a Guggenheim Fellow and member of the Institute for Advanced Study at Princeton, New Jersey. He has served as an editor of the *Journal of Symbolic Logic*, and in 1962 was elected to a three-year term as President of the Association for Symbolic Logic and as member-at-large of the Council of the American Mathematical Society.

S. C. KLEENE, Professor of Mathematics at the University of Wisconsin, received his doctorate from Princeton in 1950. In 1935 he went to the University of Wisconsin, where he has been chairman of both the Department of Mathematics and the Department of Numerical Analysis. He has served as president of the Association for Symbolic Logic and of the International Union of the History and Philosophy of Science. For twelve years he was editor of the *Journal of Symbolic Logic*. He has been awarded a Guggenheim Fellowship and also devoted a year to research at the University of Marburg under a National Science Foundation grant. He is the author of many articles on mathematical logic and foundations and of *Introduction to Metamathematics* and *The Foundation Intuitionistic Mathematics* (with R. E. Wesley).

ISAAC LEVI, Associate Professor of Philosophy at Western Reserve University, was educated at New York University and at Columbia University (Ph.D. 1957). He was a member of the faculty of philosophy at the City College of New York and has taught at Columbia University. His publications are concerned chiefly with the relevance of probability and decision theory to scientific inference.

SIDNEY MORGENBESSER, Professor of Philosophy at Columbia University, received his Ph.D. degree from the University of Pennsylvania (1956). He is a Guggenheim Fellow (1963), Editor of the *Journal of Philosophy*, and Chairman, Conference on Methods (1964–1966). He has edited *Readings in the Philosophy of Science* (with Arthur C. Danto) and *Freedom of the Will* (with James J. Walsh).

ERNEST NAGEL, author and John Dewey Professor of Philosophy at Columbia University, was educated at the College of the City of New York and at Columbia University. Dr. Nagel joined the faculty of Columbia University in 1931. He is a past president of the Association for Symbolic Logic and a past president of the American Philosophical Association. A Fellow of the Association for the Advancement of Science, he is vice-president of the Institute for the Unity of Science. Since 1940, Dr. Nagel has been editor of the *Journal of Philosophy*. He has been awarded two Guggenheim fellowships and is the author or co-author of numerous works in the field of philosophy.

HILARY PUTNAM, Professor of Philosophy at Harvard University, was educated at the University of Pennsylvania, Harvard, and the University of California at Los Angeles (Ph.D. 1951). He has been the recipient of Rockefeller and Guggenheim fellowships and of a grant from the Minnesota Center for the Philosophy of Science. He also held the Jonathan Edwards Preceptorship at Princeton University. His publications have been numerous in the fields of philosophy and mathematical logic.

WILLARD V. QUINE, Professor of Philosophy at Harvard (Edgar Pierce chair), was educated at Oberlin College and Harvard (Ph.D. 1932). Dr. Quine has been the recipient of honorary degrees from Oberlin College and Ohio State University. He studied at the universities of Vienna, Prague, and Warsaw. He has been visiting professor at Oxford and lecturer at London University and at universities in Japan and Australia. He is author of *Mathematical Logic, Word and Object,* and *Set Theory and Its Logic.* Dr. Quine is a past president of the Association for Symbolic Logic and of the American Philosophical Association (Eastern division). He is a member of the British Academy, American Academy of Arts and Sciences, American Philosophical Society, and Institut Internationale de Philosophie.

MICHAEL SCRIVEN, Professor of Philosophy at the University of California, Berkeley, was educated at the University of Melbourne, Australia, and at Oxford (Ph.D. 1956). His teaching activities have also found him at the University of Minnesota and at Swarthmore College. In 1962, he was awarded a fellowship to engage in research at the Center for Advanced Study of Behavioral Sciences, Stanford University. He is co-author and co-editor of the *Minnesota Studies in the Philosophy of Science* and is a contributor of articles and reviews to *Contemporary Psychology*.

PATRICK SUPPES, Professor of Philosophy and Statistics at Stanford University, was educated at the University of Chicago and at Columbia University (Ph.D. 1950). He has been at Stanford since 1950 and has served there as Associate Dean of Humanities and Social Sciences. His special fields are the philosophy of science and logic and mathematical methods in the social sciences. He is the author of several books, including *Introduction to Logic* and *Axiomatic Set Theory,* and numerous articles and textbooks. He was secretary-general of the International Congress for Logic, Methodology and the Philosophy of Science and is prominent in many professional and learned societies.

Introduction

Sidney Morgenbesser

This volume, containing essays by many of our leading logicians and philosophers of science, should rebut the familiar charge that philosophy of science lacks vision and has become so technical that its results are communicable and are of interest only to specialists.

Most if not all the authors accept the thesis that is defended in the opening essay by Ernest Nagel—that science is best understood as a quest for knowledge. To adopt that thesis is not to deny that science has other aspects or to insist that scientific knowledge is the only form of knowledge or to claim that knowledge alone is of value. I apologize for these banalities, but some seem to agree with D. H. Lawrence's claim that "the philosopher because he can think decides that nothing but thought matters." Here it is forgotten that the philosopher does not deny that he has a body when he discovers that he can use his head.

General discussions of the nature and goals of science, though necessary, obviously do not constitute a philosophy of science. They must be supplemented by the analysis of key terms used by science and those employed to discuss specific theories (see, for example, the chapters by S. C. Kleene and Leon Henkin) and by the elucidation of specific scientific theories. Such clarification and elucidation often require the employment of modern logical tools and theories, which are also indispensable when we attempt to offer acceptable and clear characterizations of the nature of scientific theory (see the chapter by Patrick Suppes).

Given such attempts at elucidation, it is understandable that many have characterized the philosophy of science as "second order" intellectual activity directed toward the clarification of "first order" scientific products. But though understandable and not completely without basis, the thesis is misleading. It suggests the falsehood that the poor scientist is inherently confused and always in need of intellectual first aid, which the philosopher is uniquely competent to administer. Moreover, the thesis does not capture the scope of the philosophy of science. It neglects to emphasize that it is intrinsic to the philosophy of science to try to codify and specify the conditions under which various types of claims that scientists make about their products can be accepted and also to criticize various claims that have been made about the scope of science and about the areas amenable to scientific study. Thus it is part of the job of the philosophy of science to try to elucidate the criteria for a satisfactory explanation (see the essays by Carl G. Hempel and Morton Beckner), to specify the conditions under which theories can be deemed acceptable on the basis of evidence and allied considerations (see the essays by Nelson Goodman, Max Black, and Hilary Putnam), and to review claims about the role of values in science and the amenability of value judgments to scientific analyses (see the essays by Isaac Levi and Michael Scriven).

Finally, the view that the philosophy of science is "second order" commentary on the sciences fails to emphasize the intimate interconnection between the philosophy of science and other branches of philosophy, especially the theory of knowledge, which has always played a key role in philosophy.

It is central to the theory of knowledge to attempt to specify criteria for and types of knowledge. And it is partly because of interest in the theory of knowledge that philosophers have been so concerned with modern developments in logic and mathematics, many of which challenge traditional distinctions between necessary and contingent truth, or between purely logical and purely factual knowledge, and force us to rethink various traditional theses about the nature of mathematical truth and mathematical systems (see the essays by Leon Henkin, S. C. Kleene, and Willard V. Quine). Developments in the so-called empirical sciences are also revelant to the issues in the theory of knowledge, especially those concerning criteria for knowledge and theses about the structure of knowledge (see the essays by Ernest Nagel and Norwood Russell Hanson). Note that the process here is a dialectical one. From Plato to our own day, philosophers have proposed criteria for knowledge and have revised them in the light of scientific knowledge, and have also criticized claims for knowledge in the light of criteria they think acceptable. Obviously, this description needs amplification and qualification; it is only a first sketch.

The same is true for other areas of philosophy—for example, ontology and metaphysics. It is a commonplace that those who discuss time, space, and causality must be acquainted with modern work in physics (see the essays by Adolf Grünbaum and Paul Feyerabend); it is equally obvious that those who discuss problems of the existence of numbers, properties, and classes must be acquainted with work in the foundations of logic and mathematics. But to go from the state of familiarity with the work of science to one of assessing it requires often not merely expert knowledge but commitment to a philosophical position which frequently can at best be only partially supported by appeal to the sciences. Of course, a philosophical position cannot be at variance with a scientific result, but it may force us to doubt whether a given scientific claim is a scientific result. Those who might here detect hubris on the part of the philosopher are reminded of Mach, Poincaré, Duhem, and other scientists; the emphasis is on the nature of the argument, not upon the profession of the men who present it.

Thus, five major goals of the philosophy of science are: to clarify the nature and aims of science; to specify the structure of particular scientific theories; to criticize and to comment critically on scientific claims in the light of epistemological and ontological theses; to assess claims about the possible reach of science; and to buttress or test various epistemological theses on the basis of scientific results. These objectives have been shared by the great philosophers of the past.

To stress these continuities is not, of course, to deny that there are some novel elements in the philosophy of science today. We began with and now refer back to the commonplace that many contemporary philosophers are convinced that formalization is necessary not merely in science but also in the philosophy science; most of them are more analytical than their predecessors. But these truisms can only be accepted as an introduction to the true story, which cannot be fully told until we move to the nether regions and try to analyze "analysis." But, still as a preliminary, we may say that philosophers who analyze and try to clarify are opposed to philosophers who think it important to deny that science is a manifestation of the human spirit at its highest and reserve that rank for philosophy or perhaps for philosophy and poetry. Many philosophers of science find themselves spiritually allied with the scientist, and don't think that they have to banish him in order to make room for the poet, or conversely. And here, as I have tried to indicate, they are at one with many of their great predecessors, from Aristotle to Kant. And, like them, they are fascinated by results in logic, mathematics, and science which have intrinsic value because they add to man's knowledge and understanding.

Contents

PHILOSOPHY OF SCIENCE TODAY

1 THE NATURE AND AIM OF SCIENCE

Ernest Nagel

Men usually give little thought to the techniques they use in solving problems, until habitual methods of resolving difficulties prove to be unsatisfactory in providing answers to new questions. In the history of science, at any rate, acute concern over methodological issues is frequently generated when customary modes of analyzing a particular subject matter seem to be inadequate, or when traditional ways of evaluating evidence and of interpreting the conclusions of inquiry appear to be defective. It is therefore not surprising that in an age like ours, so strongly marked by scientific revolutions as well as by social upheavals, much intensive thought should be given by practicing scientists and professional philosophers to the logic of science and to the broad significance of scientific achievements. The contemporary literature on the philosophy of science is at bottom a critical response to some of the intellectual difficulties created by recent developments in science.

There are, in fact, three aspects of contemporary science that invite serious reflection and help to define its nature and aim; and I want to say something about each of them, even though it is impossible to do justice to them in brief compass.

1. Perhaps the most obvious feature of science, and undoubtedly the one that has been most publicized, is the practical control over nature which science yields. It would be tedious to rehearse the great contributions of scientific inquiry to human welfare, or even to mention the major branches of technology, such as medicine, which profited from advances in fundamental theoretical and experimental research. It is sufficient to note that

3

applied science has transformed the face of the earth and has brought into being our contemporary Western civilization.

Since it is the technological fruits of scientific inquiry that can be most readily appreciated by men without scientific training or theoretical interests, to most people the practical mastery over nature that often follows from fundamental research is the ultimate justification of science. Indeed, because the heavy financial costs of carrying on scientific inquiry today must be paid in large measure from public funds, many scientists tend to stress almost exclusively the practical benefits to be expected from basic research when they describe the nature of science to general audiences who must, after all, ultimately shoulder the major part of the costs.

However, although I would not for a moment underestimate the importance of science as a source of improved and expanding technologies that contribute to the enhancement of human life, I believe, nevertheless, that the conception of science as the golden goose endlessly producing practical controls over nature has been overemphasized to the neglect of its other aspects. It is certainly not true that the achievement of useful goods and services is the sole, or even the main, motive which actuates men in their pursuit of scientific inquiry; and when such a motive is made focal, a badly distorted picture is created of both the complex goals and the actual history of science.

Moreover, such an emphasis tends to generate a socially dangerous image of the scientist as an infallible miracle worker who is bound to have a sure answer for every human ill. Nor should one overlook the widespread tendency to make the scientific enterprise inherently responsible for the barbarous uses to which the findings of science are sometimes put—an undoubtedly mistaken imputation which can lead to the impairment of science, but which appears plausible when science is identified with its technological fruits.

2. In point of fact, science assumes a second aspect when it is viewed as directed to the attainment of systematic but reliable *knowledge,* so that its products are taken to be warranted *conclusions* about more or less extensive uniform conditions under which various kinds of events take place. Indeed, according to an

4

ancient and still sound formula, the aim of science is "to save the phenomena"—that is, to exhibit events and processes as instances of general laws and theories which formulate invariable patterns of relations between things. In pursuing this aim, science seeks to make the world intelligible; and whenever it achieves this objective in some area of inquiry, science satisfies the craving to know and understand, which is perhaps the most powerful impulse that leads men to engage in systematic inquiry. As a consequence of its generally successful pursuit of this aim, the enterprise which started in Greek antiquity and which we call "science" has been a major force in the development of liberal civilization: it has served to undermine superstitious beliefs and practices, to dissolve fears that thrive on ignorance, and to supply the intellectual basis for evaluating inherited customs and traditional rules of conduct.

It would, of course, be flying in the face of overwhelming evidence to deny that long before the beginnings of systematic inquiry men had acquired fairly reliable knowledge about many features of their physical, biological, and social environment. Indeed, even today a good deal of the information we need for the normal conduct of our lives is not the product of systematic scientific inquiry but is usually designated as "common-sense" knowledge.

Nevertheless, such common-sense knowledge is marked by a number of serious limitations, some of which should be noted. Thus, common-sense beliefs are generally imprecise and often lump together things and processes which differ in crucial respects; common-sense beliefs are frequently mutually inconsistent, so that the adoption of one rather than another of two incompatible beliefs as the basis for action is arbitrary; common-sense beliefs tend to be highly fragmented, so that logical as well as substantive relations between independently asserted statements are usually ignored; common-sense beliefs are generally accepted with little awareness of the range of their sound application; common-sense beliefs are by and large myopically utilitarian, they are largely concerned with matters that impinge directly on immediately practical interests, and they are normally adequate only within areas of fairly routine experience. Finally and above all, common-sense beliefs usually disregard alternative possibilities for handling concrete problems, so that their continued acceptance is based on the authority of uncriticized custom and therefore cannot readily be modified so as to make them reliable guides in dealing with novel situations.

Although no sharp line can be drawn between common-sense assertions and the conclusions of scientific inquiry—indeed, all scientific inquiry takes its point of departure from common-sense beliefs and distinctions, and eventually supports its findings in part by falling back upon such common sense—it is a distinctive mark of science that it deliberately attempts to produce conclusions freed from the limitations of common sense, or possessing those limitations to a lesser degree.

Moreover, while the extent to which such conclusions are achieved varies with the different branches of science, and is undoubtedly greatest in the natural sciences, no branch of systematic inquiry is wholly unsuccessful in this attempt. In general, the conclusions of scientific inquiry are better supported by competent evidence, and have a better claim to be counted as reliable knowledge, than common-sense beliefs. I will have something further to say on this point. For the moment, however, I want to make clear that despite the general reliability of scientific findings, neither scientific reports about specific matters of fact nor the theories and laws taken to formulate invariable conditions under which phenomena occur are infallibly true and in principle incorrigible.

It was indeed once taken for granted that a proposition to be genuinely a scientific one, it must be established as indubitably certain and recognized as absolutely necessary. Taking deductive geometry as the paradigm, this view maintained that science is not content with merely ascertaining what the facts are, but seeks to demonstrate that the facts must be as they are and could not be otherwise; however, since to establish a statement demonstratively there must be premises which in the end cannot themselves be demonstrated, the basic premises of a science were required to be capable of being grasped as self-evidently and necessarily true.

This conception of the nature of science was understandably

plausible at a time when Euclidean geometry was the only known example of systematized knowledge, and it continues to be endorsed by many contemporary thinkers who subscribe to the belief that "the universe is rational," so that "there can be no residuum of irrational (that is, contingently true) facts in the whole of science." Nevertheless, in the light of the subsequent history of science such a conception is untenable. For no basic assumptions of any science dealing with matters of fact are actually self-evident, and progress of inquiry in every branch of science has revealed that the principles once accepted as basic had to be modified or replaced by others if the principles were to be adequate to newly discovered fact. This thesis that all so-called first principles of science are in principle corrigible is clearly illustrated by contemporary developments in physics, which has been making radical revisions in theoretical assumptions that were once regarded as indubitable.

However, such revisions of basic assumptions cannot rightly be construed as signs of the "bankruptcy" of modern science—a characterization frequently made by thinkers who are wedded to the mistaken notion of classical rationalism that unless science can guarantee its conclusions to be unshakably certain, it has failed to produce genuine knowledge. Moreover, such revisions do not warrant a wholesale skepticism concerning the possibility of obtaining reliable knowledge of the world by way of scientific inquiry—a skepticism which is again induced by the untenable assumption that since every conclusion of scientific inquiry is in principle corrigible, no such conclusion is in fact a stable addition to the corpus of reliable knowledge. Let me cite but one example which belies this last assumption and at the same time illustrates how by providing well-founded explanations for observed phenomena, science satisfies the perennial quest for systematic knowledge and understanding.

Galileo noted that there appears to be an upper limit to the size of animals such as man, and raised the question whether, despite appearances, men with giant proportions might at some time have walked on the face of the earth. He showed by careful experiment that the strength of a beam varies with its cross section, and assumed on reasonable grounds that the ability of animal bones to withstand a crushing stress also varies with the area of their cross sections. On the other hand, the weight of a terrestrial animal (which must be supported by its limbs) is proportional to the animal's volume. Accordingly, the strength of animal bones is proportional to the *square* of an animal's linear dimensions, while the weight those bones must support is proportional to the *cube* of its linear dimensions. In consequence, there are definite limits to the size of terrestrial animals, so that giants with limbs proportional to those of ordinary men could not exist, since such creatures would collapse under their own weight.

Galileo's conclusion and the assumptions on which he based it have not been substantially modified, though they have been refined and made more precise by inquiry during the subsequent three centuries. The example thus supports the thesis that despite the corrigibility of scientific findings, the content of science is not an unstable flux of opinion, but that, on the contrary, science can succeed in its aim of supplying reliable, well-founded, systematic explanations for innumerable phenomena.

3. It is time, however, to consider the third aspect that science presents: its method of inquiry. This aspect is often misconceived and is in any case difficult to describe briefly, but is perhaps the most permanent feature of science and the ultimate warrant for confidence in the conclusions of scientific inquiry.

It is frequently said, however, even by distinguished scientists, that "there is no scientific method as such," but only "the free and utmost use of intelligence." This contention is well founded if the term "scientific method" is taken to denote some generally accepted set of fixed rules for the discovery of solutions to any problem. A historically influential approach to the analysis of scientific method does in fact place considerable, if not exclusive, stress upon the task of formulating precepts for finding the causes or effects of phenomena, and for deriving laws or theories from materials of observation. However, none of the proposed rules for making discoveries achieve their intended objective, and most students of the subject agree that the construction of such rules is a hopeless undertaking.

What, then, is scientific method? But I must first make clear that "method" must not be construed as synonymous with "technique." Thus, the technique of measuring wave lengths of light with a spectroscope is patently different from the technique of measuring the speed of a nerve impulse, and both are manifestly different from the techniques employed in determining the effects upon production of a given type of factory organization. In general, therefore, techniques differ with the subject being investigated and may change rapidly with advances in technology. On the other hand, all the sciences use a common method in their inquiries, insofar as they employ the same principles in evaluating the weight of evidence, the same canons for judging the adequacy of proposed explanations, and the same criteria for deciding between alternative hypotheses.

In short, scientific method is the general logic employed, whether tacitly or explicitly, for assessing the merits of an inquiry. It is, therefore, helpful to think of scientific method as constituted by a set of norms which serve as standards that must be satisfied if any inquiry is to count as a responsibly conducted one whose conclusions merit rational confidence. I want now to discuss briefly a few salient elements of scientific method so understood.

It is well to begin with the reminder that science is a social institution, and that scientists are members of a self-governing intellectual community, dedicated to the pursuit of truth in a manner conforming to standards that have evolved and have proved to be sound in a continuing process of mutual criticism. Many thinkers have supposed that the objectivity of conclusions reached in science is assured if scientists resolve as individuals to accept no proposition which is in the least doubtful and is not transparently true. However, men are usually unaware of the many tacit assumptions involved in what they regard as indubitable, and they frequently believe themselves to be making no intellectual commitments of any kind, although in fact they are tacitly subscribing to much that is false.

Accordingly, while resolutions to be critical of the assumptions one makes may have a certain value, the objectivity of science is not primarily a consequence of such resolutions. On the contrary, that objectivity is the product of a community of thinkers, each

9

offering unsparing criticisms of cognitive claims that the others make. For no one scientist engaged in this process of criticism is infallible, and each has his own peculiar intellectual or emotional bias. But the biases are rarely the same; and ideas which can survive the cross fire of the varied critical commentary that a large number of independently acting minds supply stand a better chance of being sound than conceptions which are alleged to be valid simply on the ground that they seem self-evident to some individual thinker.

Let me next comment on the popular view, sometimes endorsed by scientists, that a scientific inquiry must begin by collecting facts, the data thus collected being then pressed through some sort of logical sieve which finally yields a uniquely determined formulation of a regularity between the events under study. But the inadequacy of this view becomes evident as soon as we remind ourselves that it is not easy to know what facts should be gathered for resolving a given problem, or whether an alleged fact really is a fact.

For example, just what data should be collected in an inquiry into the causes of leukemia? Is the moon really larger when it is near the horizon than when it is at the zenith? The number of facts that could be noted is legion, and they cannot all be examined; and what is reported as a fact may be an illusion. It is therefore clear that facts must be selected on the basis of assumptions as to which ones are *relevant* for resolving a given problem, and observations must be conducted under conditions which are assumed to exclude the possibility that reports of what is allegedly observed are not grossly in error. Accordingly, any significant gathering of facts for the purposes of scientific inquiry is controlled by assumption of various kinds which must be supplied by the inquiring scientist and not by the subject of his research. In particular, since facts do not proclaim themselves to be relevant or irrelevant for a given problem, the scientist must adopt at least some preliminary hypothesis as to what sorts of facts are pertinent to his problem—for example, which of the innumerable factors that may conceivably be present in his subject matter are causally related to the phenomenon he is studying—so that until he replaces it by another, this preliminary hypothesis directs his investigations.

Without such hypotheses, inquiry is aimless and blind. However, there are no rules for constructing valuable hypotheses; and as Albert Einstein repeatedly observed, those systems of hypotheses that constitute the theories of modern physics are "free creations of the mind," requiring for their invention and elaboration feats of imagination quite analogous to creative effort in the arts.

Nevertheless, though the role of creative imagination in scientific inquiry must be recognized, science is neither poetry nor unsupported speculation; and hypotheses which are introduced in the conduct of inquiry, as well as other proposed explanations for some class of phenomena, must be tested. In general, such testing involves an examination of the congruence of a hypothesis (or of its logical consequences), in part with observed matters of fact and in part with other hypotheses whose concordance with observed fact has already been established.

A detailed account of the logic of testing hypotheses cannot be given here, but brief mention must be made of the notion of a *controlled inquiry*—perhaps the most important single element in that logic. A simple example must suffice to indicate what characterizes such inquiries. The belief, widely held at one time, that cold salt water baths were beneficial to patients suffering from high fevers seems to have been based on repeated observations of subsequent improvement in the condition of patients subjected to this treatment. However, irrespective of whether or not the belief is sound—in point of fact, it is not—the evidence on which it was based is insufficient to establish its validity. It apparently did not occur to those who accepted the belief on that evidence to ask whether patients not given such treatment might show a similar improvement. In short, the belief was not the product of a controlled inquiry—that is, the course of the disease in patients receiving the treatment was not compared with its course in a control group who did not receive it, so that there was no rational basis for deciding whether the treatment made any difference.

More generally, an inquiry is a controlled one only if, by instituting some kind of *eliminative* procedure, the *differential* effects of a factor that is assumed to be relevant to the occurrence of a given phenomenon can be ascertained. Such an eliminative procedure is sometimes, but not necessarily, an overtly experimental one, since in many domains and for the most part overt experiments are not feasible, so that quite complicated and subtle analytical tools must frequently be used to extract from the available evidence the information needed for a rational decision on the merits of a hypothesis. But, in one form or another, control is an essential ingredient in the logic of scientific method—for by and large, the reliability of scientific conclusions is a function of the multiplicity and of the rigor of the controls to which such conclusions have been subjected.

I would like, finally, to comment briefly on the role of quantitative distinctions and measurement in furthering the aims of science and in augmenting the dependability of its cognitive claims. Although there are important structural differences between various quantitative determinations, all types of measurement have a threefold function. One is to increase the precision, and thereby to diminish the vagueness, with which alleged facts and explanations for them may be formulated, so that the formulations can in consequence be more easily tested. The second is to make possible finer discriminations of traits in various subject-matters, so that statements about them may thereby be subjected to more rigorous controls. The third is to permit more comprehensive comparisons between diverse events, so that relations between things may be systematically and accurately formulated. It is therefore quite erroneous to maintain, as is often done, that the so-called quantitative sciences which make extensive use of measurement ignore the qualitative aspects of reality. How unfounded this allegation is will be evident from a single example.

Human beings are able to distinguish between a certain number of differences in the warmth of objects, and terms like "hot," "very warm," "warm," "lukewarm," "cool," and "cold" correspond to such recognized distinctions. But these differences were not ignored or denied when the thermometer was invented in the seventeenth century; on the contrary, the invention of this instrument signalized the fact that variations in experienced differences in the warmth of many substances were found to be connected with changes in the relative volumes of those substances. In consequence, variations in volume can be taken to represent changes in the physical state of a body, changes which in some cases correspond to felt differences in their warmth. Moreover, it is possible to recognize finer differences in variations of volume than in directly experienced changes of warmth; and there are extremes of hot and cold beyond which human beings are unable to discriminate any further, although volume changes beyond these limits can still be distinguished. Accordingly, by using a thermometric scale we do not ignore qualitative differences; the use of that scale permits us to note differences in qualities which would otherwise escape our attention, and it also enables us to order those qualities in an unambiguous and uniform manner.

To sum up: The major impulse which generates science is the desire for explanations that are at once systematic and controllable by factual evidence. The distinctive aim of science is therefore the discovery and the formulation in general terms of the conditions under which events of various kinds occur, the generalized statements of such determining conditions serving as explanations of the corresponding happenings. This goal can be achieved only by distinguishing or isolating certain properties in the subject matters studied, and by ascertaining the repeatable patterns of dependence in which those properties stand to one another. In consequence, when an inquiry is successful, propositions that hitherto appeared to be quite unrelated are shown to be linked to each other in determinate ways by virtue of their place in some system of explanations.

It is of primary importance, however, to regard such explanatory systems, not as a body of fixed and indubitable conclusions, but rather as the corrigible products of a continuing process of inquiry that involves the indefatigable use of a distinctive intellectual method of criticism. It is this logical method which is the special glory of modern science as well as the spiritual foundation of every genuinely liberal civilization. There are no reasonable alternatives to it for arriving at responsibly supported conclusions about the world men inhabit and men's place in it.

2 TRUTH AND PROVABILITY

Leon Henkin

The word "truth," as well as such words as "beauty" and "justice," refers to concepts so broad, and so deeply stirring to the human spirit, that some have set them as the aim of life. Here, however, we shall limit ourselves to a much narrower concept of truth, namely, as an attribute of sentences: What does it mean to say that a sentence is true?

We find this question discussed in some of the earliest philosophical writings known to us, and it has attracted the attention of philosophers continuously since then. But here we shall discuss a mathematical solution to the question. As with every scientific discovery, it is possible to trace a long chain of historical events contributing to the ultimate solution. But the decisive conception and formulation of the mathematical theory of truth was made about thirty years ago by Alfred Tarski.

The distinction between true and false is made in the case of those sentences which purport to convey information about some realm, either empirical or abstract. Thus the notion of truth which concerns us is a *relation* connecting certain symbolic arrays (that is, sentences) with a domain to which these refer. And for a definition of this relation to be considered adequate, it must specify, for *every* sentence, exactly under which states (or conditions) of the domain the sentence is considered true.

Now if we select just one sentence, and ask under what conditions *it* is true, we get a deceptively simple solution. For example, the sentence "Copper is a metal" is true if, and only if, copper is a metal. At first sight this specification of truth conditions seems to express something so obvious that one is led to suspect it may convey no information at all—like the sentence "Stockholm is Stockholm," for example. But closer examination reveals that this is not so.

To see this, let us introduce the letter Q as a name for the sentence "Copper is a metal." Then our specification of the truth conditions for this sentence can be expressed by saying: *The sentence Q is true if, and only if, copper is a metal.* In this form we see clearly that a *name* of the sentence "Copper is a metal," in particular, the letter "Q," appears preceding the phrase "if and only if," while the sentence "Copper is a metal" *itself* appears after that phrase. The difference between the name of an object, and the object itself, is fundamental. Notice that we *cannot* rephrase our specification of truth conditions for Q by saying: *The sentence Q is true if, and only if, Q.* Such a rephrasing makes no sense, for after the phrase "if and only if" the rules of grammar require that a sentence appear, not the name of a sentence.

Intuitively, we see that the idea used to specify the truth conditions of the sentence Q can be used equally well for any other sentence—or for several sentences considered together. Thus, if P is the sentence "Grass is red," and if R is the sentence "Tomorrow is either Monday or Friday," we can give the conditions of truth for these sentences by specifying: P is true just in case grass is red, and R is true just in case tomorrow is either Monday or Friday.

Now *if* we held the view that the totality of sentences is finite, we could conceive of a complete specification of the notion of truth along the lines here indicated. That is, we could imagine first constructing a complete list of all sentences, and then for each one of them we could specify truth conditions in the manner employed above for P, Q, and R. For many reasons—such as its great length—such a "definition" of truth would be highly unsatisfactory. But the most decisive point against it is our unwillingness to admit that there are only a finite number of sentences. Even though only finitely many sentences have been formulated by people to date, our idea of language leaves open the possibility of forming an unlimited number of increasingly complex sentences in the future. What we need, then, is a single definition of "true sentence," finite in length, of course, which will encompass all of the infinitely many truth conditions of the kind considered above for individual sentences.

To deal with the infinitude of sentences, we need to use the fact that every sentence is put together from a finite number of symbols, according to grammatical laws. This suggests the use of what mathematicians call a *recursive* definition, based upon a structural analysis of sentences. In other words, the definition would first specify truth conditions for the shortest kind of sentences (called *elementary* sentences). And then the definition would go on to indicate how truth conditions for any complex sentence S can be obtained from the truth conditions of the component elementary sentences out of which S is constructed.

There are several difficulties which beset such a plan, of which we shall mention two. The first is the fact that for any of the natural languages known to us—whether it be English, Swahili, or Sanskrit—the grammatical rules of sentence formation are not only very complicated but (from a mathematician's viewpoint) hopelessly imprecise. Thus it appears that one of the difficulties encountered in attempting to specify what we mean by "true sentence" is that we have the greatest difficulty in saying what "sentence" means!

A second difficulty which must be faced by any proposed definition of truth is connected with certain paradoxes which have been known to philosophers since antiquity. Of these, the most direct is the so-called Paradox of the Liar, which we can formulate as follows.

We know that certain sentences can make assertions about themselves; the following one, for example, is true: "This sentence contains five words." Now let us consider another sentence which asserts something about itself, and inquire whether *it* is true. The sentence we have in mind—which we shall call X in the sequel—is the following: "This sentence is false."

Now let us *assume,* for the moment, that the sentence X is true. We conclude that what X asserts must be correct, that is, that X is false. So if we *assume* that X is true, we *conclude* that X is also false.

Next, let us *assume* that X is false. Then, since X asserts its own falsity, we conclude that it is correct. In other words, if we *assume* that X is false, we *conclude* that it is also true.

We seem to have shown that whether X is assumed to be true or false, we can conclude that it is *both* true and false. This violates our fundamental conception of the distinction between true and false sentences.

The two problems we have mentioned, namely, imprecise rules of sentence formation and the possibility of formulating paradoxes, provide convincing evidence that in fact it is *not possible* to give a satisfactory definition of "true sentence" which will encompass the totality of sentences of a natural language. Accordingly, Tarski turned his attention to certain *artificial* languages of a kind which had been studied in the first two decades of this century.

How these languages came to be developed we shall relate below. At the moment, we need only note that the rules of sentence formation for these languages are given with mathematical precision, and that each of the languages is designed to express facts about a limited scientific area. It is the resulting limitation on vocabulary which excludes such paradoxical sentences as X from these languages.

Working with these languages Tarski was able to give a mathematically precise definition of "true sentence" having the following two properties. First, the definition has a recursive character which permits one to obtain truth conditions for any complex sentence, by analyzing its syntactical structure, in terms of the meanings of its elementary parts. Second, from the definition one can establish in a mathematical way certain general laws about the truth concept, of which a simple example is the law of excluded middle: For every sentence S, either S is true or not-S is true.

We do not have space to present Tarski's definition in detail. But perhaps we can give some idea of its character, and of the problems which it overcomes, through several illustrations.

One way to obtain increasingly long sentences is to combine shorter sentences repeatedly by means of the so-called *connectives,* such as the words "and" and "or." The truth condition for a compound sentence of this kind can be obtained easily from the truth conditions for its component sentences, by means of certain clauses of Tarski's definition which are supplied for each of the connectives. For example, one of these clauses specifies that a conjunctive compound of the form *P and Q* will be true if, and only if, *P* is true and *Q* is true.

On the other hand, suppose we are dealing with a language which refers to the non-negative integers, 0, 1, 2, 3, etc. If the language contains an equality sign, a plus sign denoting addition, and the numerals "1" and "2," then we can form increasingly long sentences, each having the simple form $f = g$, by repeated use of the plus sign. For example, among these sentences would be $(2 + 2) = 1$, and $(2 + 1 + 1 + 1 + 2) = (1 + 1 + 2 + 2)$. Now we observe that no matter how long a sentence of this kind may be, it contains no shorter sentence which is a part of it; the length is due solely to the number of plus signs used on each side of the equation. Hence, in order to obtain truth conditions for sentences of this kind, we cannot use the previous device of referring to truth conditions for component sentences. Instead, we must concern ourselves with the integers which are denoted by the long expressions on each side of the equality sign. This illustrates the general situation that sentences are built up not only from shorter sentences but from components coming from several grammatical categories. For this reason a recursive definition of truth must deal simultaneously with other semantical notions, such as denotation.

As a last illustration consider the following sentence, in which the letters *x* and *y* serve as variables to refer to arbitrary integers: "For every integer *x* there is an integer *y* such that $y > x$." As it happens, we can see easily enough that this sentence is true. If, however, we seek to analyze its grammatical structure, we see that one of its components is the formula "$y > x$." This formula resembles certain sentences, such as "$3 > 2$" and "$5 > 7$," but the formula "$y > x$" is *not* itself a sentence, for by itself it is neither true nor false. A formula of this kind, containing variables, is called a *sentential formula*. Since it is necessary to deal with these in a recursive definition of "true sentence," Tarski employed a special semantical notion appropriate to them. This is the notion of a sequence of objects (in our case integers) *satisfy-*

ing a formula. Tarski's treatment of expressions containing variables is often considered the key idea in his definition of truth.

It must be emphasized that while the definition furnishes, for each sentence *S,* a statement specifying the *conditions* under which *S* is true, it does *not* furnish the information as to whether *S* is in *fact* true. For instance, we can infer from the definition that the sentence "Grass is red" will be true just in case grass is red. But the definition gives no information about the color of grass. Hence in order to determine whether this sentence is in fact true, we must combine our knowledge of the definition with an empirical investigation.

To determine the truth or falsity of a given empirical sentence, by direct verification of its truth condition, may sometimes be so arduous a task as to be completely impractical. In case of a mathematical sentence, the situation may be even worse. For instance, if the sentence ascribes some property to each of the infinitely many numbers 0, 1, 2, 3, etc., we may see no possibility, in principle, of concluding a direct verification.

Fortunately, we have another method to establish the truth of a sentence, *S,* quite different from direct verification. Namely, we may *infer* the truth of *S* from a knowledge of the truth of certain *other* sentences, say *T, U,* and *V.* To establish such an inference, we provide a series of intermediate sentences, leading from *T, U,* and *V* to *S.* Such a chain of sentences is called a *deduction;* the starting sentences, *T, U,* and *V,* are called the *hypotheses* of the deduction; and the final sentence *S* is called the *conclusion.* Each sentence of the deduction must be obtained from the preceding ones according to a so-called "law of logic." These laws are simple to apply, and are supposed to possess the property that they never lead from true sentences to a false one.

We sometimes attempt to organize our knowledge in a certain domain, say *D,* by seeking to infer all of the true sentences dealing with *D* from one fixed set of hypotheses. By so doing we create a *theory* of the domain *D;* the fixed hypotheses are then called *axioms* of the theory; deductions starting from the axioms are called *proofs;* and conclusions reached by proofs are called *theorems.*

Everyone will recognize that the prototype for axiomatic

theories of this kind is to be found in Euclid's work on geometry. Portions of physics were axiomatized at the time of Newton. And during the last hundred years the process of axiomatization has been refined and extended to every part of pure and applied mathematics.

It is curious, that during the many centuries in which mathematicians studied and constructed proofs, the laws of logic employed in passing to each new step of a proof were never explicitly formulated—except for those very simple cases investigated by Aristotle. But beginning with George Boole, who worked in England around 1850, increasing attention was bestowed on this problem by mathematicians. Their approach to logic was built on Aristotle's recognition that laws of logic are to be expressed in *formal* terms; that is to say, any such law relates the structural form of a conclusion to the corresponding forms of the hypotheses. But mathematical logicians realized that the forms involved in most proofs are much more complex than those which were treated by Aristotle.

In order to deal in a mathematical way with the necessary complexity of sentential forms, modern logicians were led to devise idealized languages. These were based upon a formalism consisting of an explicit list of symbols arranged in several classes, together with formal rules for combining the symbols into sentences. Any such language is capable of expressing only a limited portion of the ideas which can be conveyed in natural language; nevertheless, some were devised which seem adequate to deal with a substantial portion, if not all, of some branch of science or of mathematics.

To the rules of sentence formation, in such a language, the logician then added a list of axioms, and of formal rules of inference, by means of which he could construct proofs. These rules were of the simplest kind, expressed purely in terms of sentential structure, such as the rule of detachment which permits passage from two sentences of the form *If Q then R* and *Q*, to the sentence *R*. In this way the logician created a fully formalized axiomatic theory, called a *formal deductive theory,* by means of which he could formulate and study the laws of logic with mathematical precision.

Because the formal rules of inference have such a simple character, it is possible to decide in a purely mechanical way whether any given chain of sentences of a formal deductive theory is or is not a proof. It is this property which makes these formal theories useful as a means of establishing theorems, for if we did not have such a mechanical means of testing proofs, we would be entitled to ask for a proof that any alleged proof was indeed a proof!

Of course even more preferable than a mechanical means of deciding which chains of sentences are proofs would be a mechanical means of deciding which sentences are theorems. Such a mechanical device, if it exists, is called a *decision procedure* for the formal deductive theory. The question whether there *is* such a procedure is the *decision problem* for the theory. These concepts will be described in some detail by S. C. Kleene in his essay "Computability."

The artificial languages devised by mathematical logicians as a basis for their formal deductive theories were precisely those languages to which Tarski had turned in developing his definition of truth. Using this definition, for any of these languages which was created to deal with a mathematical domain, it is a simple matter to demonstrate, first, that each axiom is a true sentence, and second, that whenever a formal rule of inference is applied to sentences which are true, the resulting sentence is also true. It follows readily that each theorem in one of these formal deductive systems—that is, each provable sentence—is true.

What is not at all clear, in general, is the converse question: Is each true sentence a theorem? In other words, is there a proof for every true sentence? This is the problem of *completeness* for the deductive theory. The study of this problem has been one of the most interesting developments of mathematical logic, and we hope in the next essay to describe these investigations in some detail. But perhaps we can conclude this chapter with a brief indication of one kind of result to which these investigations led.

It is clear enough that *some* deductive theories will *not* be complete. This will generally be the case, for example, if we select very few axioms and rules of inference, or if we start with a complete system and then discard some of the axioms or rules. The unexpected discovery, however, was that in the case of languages dealing with certain domains, it is impossible to obtain a complete deductive system!

To see the reason for this, we revert to our consideration of the paradoxes. The possibility of formulating these paradoxes in natural language, which rests upon the fact that the concept of *true sentence* can be expressed within this language itself, was used as evidence that no satisfactory definition of truth can be given for the totality of sentences of such a language. Put another way, for any language for which a satisfactory definition of truth *can* be given, it must be impossible to express the concept of *true sentence* within that language itself.

On the other hand, it turns out that among the languages for which a satisfactory definition of truth can be given we can find one with the following property: No matter how we select axioms and rules of inference to obtain a formal deductive theory for this language, the resulting notion of *provable sentence* can be expressed *in the language itself*. This possibility arises because the axioms and rules of inference selected are always required to be so simple as to admit a mechanical method for checking proofs.

It follows that no matter which formal deductive theory we select for such a language, the resulting notion of *provable sentence* will differ from that of *true sentence*—since the former can be expressed in the language itself while the latter cannot. Thus, all of these theories are incomplete.

3 COMPLETENESS

Leon Henkin

The logical concept of completeness connects the two notions of truth and provability which I discussed in the preceding chapter. Let me begin by recalling briefly the significance of these terms.

Truth and provability are both properties of sentences. A sentence of a language is true if it is related in a certain way to objects of a domain which is generally external to the language; a sentence is provable if it is related in a certain way to other sentences of the language itself.

More specifically, the notion of truth arises in the context of languages employed for communication about some domain, either empirical or abstract; roughly, a sentence is true if the information it conveys about this domain is correct. The notion of provability arises in the context of languages which are endowed with a deductive apparatus consisting of axioms and rules of logical inference; a sentence is provable if it can be reached by a finite sequence of intermediate sentences, starting from the axioms, each step of the sequence being obtained from earlier steps by one of the rules of inference.

The use of language to communicate, of course, preceded the formulation of axiomatic theories. In fact, these theories were devised, in part, to help establish the truth of certain sentences. For this reason axioms and rules of inference are generally chosen so as to permit ready verification that each provable sentence is true. The question whether, conversely, every true sentence is provable, is the problem of completeness. We note, therefore, that a question of completeness always presupposes a given *language*, a given *interpretation* of the language by means of which its sentences convey information about some domain, and a given *axiomatic theory* formulated within the language.

The notions of truth and provability are familiar to us, in an intuitive way, in the context of natural language. And in this context, they have long been discussed and analyzed by philosophers. However, when mathematicians began to investigate these notions (about 1850), they found it imperative to proceed to a consideration of certain idealized languages in order to make possible the application of mathematical methods. For these languages it was possible to formulate the notions of truth and provability with utmost precision, and hence to open the way for a mathematical attack on the problems of completeness.

In order to describe the results obtained, it is necessary first to indicate an important transformation which the concept of an axiomatic theory has undergone during the last one hundred years. This transformation came about through the realization that a given system of symbols and sentences can be subjected to more than one interpretation, so that a single language can be employed to refer simultaneously to many different domains. Although this possibility was implicit in work at least as early as Descartes' discovery of analytic geometry, its significance for axiomatic mathematics was not appreciated until the invention of non-Euclidean geometry by Bolyai, Lobachevsky, and Gauss in the last century.

It will be recalled that Euclid's work on geometry, which long served as the prototype for axiomatic theories, begins by defining the terms such as "point" and "line" appearing in the axioms, and subsequently defines further terms, such as "straight angle" and "circle," which appear in the formulation of theorems. Although the later definitions enter into proofs of theorems in an essential manner, it is curious that no use is made by Euclid of the definitions given at the beginning of his work!

Gradually mathematicians came to realize that not only are such definitions unnecessary but that in a sense they are improper. For just as all proofs in a theory must start ultimately from sentences which remain unproved in that theory (that is, the axioms), in order to avoid circularity, so all definitions must rest ultimately on terms which remain undefined in the theory —the so-called *primitive* terms.

Now just because the primitive terms are undefined in an axiomatic theory, we may contemplate giving them a variety of meanings. Of course under some interpretations of these terms, the axioms may turn out to be false. But any interpretation which renders the axioms true will be one for which all theorems must also be true—for the logical rules of inference, by which we pass from axioms to theorems, can never lead from true sentences to a false one. The same observation explains how, by finding an interpretation of the primitive terms of geometry which makes Euclid's parallel postulate false while all other axioms become true, one demonstrates that the parallel postulate is not derivable from the others.

The realization that sentences proved in an axiomatic theory give information simultaneously for a great many domains has had a revolutionary effect on both pure and applied mathematics. As regards applications, it meant that by moving to a more abstract level one could achieve a great economy of effort, handling problems from diverse domains by means of a single investigation. As regards pure mathematics, it led to a type of investigation in which the traditional role of language is completely reversed: Instead of starting with a fixed domain and inquiring which sentences are true about it, one starts with fixed sentences and seeks to analyze the totality of domains in which these are true.

The multiplicity of interpretations possible for the primitive terms of idealized languages, of the kind studied by logicians, has led to an extension of the completeness concept which we now describe.

Let us use the term "model" (for a given language L) to mean a domain of objects together with an interpretation whereby the symbols of L are made to refer to this domain. Such a model determines each sentence of L as true or false.

Now suppose that J is a formal deductive theory, consisting of axioms and rules of inference formulated for the language L. As we have indicated above, our notion of completeness for the theory J is relative to a given model. To make this explicit, we say that *J is complete for the model M* if every sentence of *L* which is true of *M* can be proved in *J*.

The more general notion of completeness which we require is relative not to a given model, but to a given *class* of models. If *C* is such a class, we say that a sentence of *L* is *valid in C* if it is true of every model in *C*. And we say that *J is complete for the class C* if every sentence of *L* which is valid in *C* can be proved in *J*. In case the class *C* happens to contain only a single model *M*, this notion of completeness reduces to the earlier one. At the other extreme, the class *C* may contain *all* models for the language *L*. A theory complete for this class is said to be *logically complete*. In general, *C* will be intermediate between these extremes.

It should be remarked that we are usually only interested in the question whether a theory *J* is complete for a model *M*, in case we know that all of the sentences provable in *J* are true of *M*. Similarly, the question whether *J* is complete for a given class *C* of models is raised only if we know that every theorem of *J* is valid in *C*.

The first explicit formulation and solution of a completeness problem is due to Emil Post. In his doctoral dissertation, written in 1919, he considered a formal deductive theory of sentential logic. This theory is based on a very fragmentary language in which the only logical symbols are those for the sentential connectives, such as "not," "and," "or," and "if . . . then." The elementary sentences which are connected by these symbols are unanalyzed, being represented simply by single letters. Although such a language can be interpreted for a very wide class of models, its sentences are not capable of expressing very detailed information about any of them.

Systems of sentential logic evolved from the earliest mathematical studies of logic. Boole himself was concerned with them; Peirce and Frege, among others, advanced their mathematical consideration later in the nineteenth century; and in the *Principia Mathematica* of Russell and Whitehead (1910), one finds sentential logic already incorporated in a fairly well-defined formal deductive system—although even here the formal rules of inference are not set forth as explicitly as one would desire.

Post's contribution was to provide explicitly a deductive theory of axioms and rules based upon this fragmentary language, to verify that all of its theorems are logically valid, and then to show that the theory is logically complete, that is, that every logically valid sentence can be formally proved.

As a byproduct of his work, Post obtained a *decision procedure* for the class of theorems of sentential logic—that is, a completely automatic method which can be applied to any sentence of the system and which indicates, after a finite number of steps, whether or not the sentence is provable.

Post's work was published in 1921. Nine years later an important advance was made by Kurt Gödel, who was able to establish similar completeness theorems for deductive theories based upon first-order predicate logic. The language of these systems, while still only a small fragment of natural language, is vastly richer in expressive power than the sentential language considered by Post.

In order to describe the nature of first-order languages, we begin by indicating the kind of structural domains which serve as models for these languages. A typical example would be the arithmetical system consisting of the set of non-negative integers, the operations of addition and multiplication for these numbers, the relation *less than* and the relation of equality for these numbers, and the special elements 0 and 1. More generally, the structures we have in mind may consist of an *arbitrary* set of elements, and any number of indicated operations, relations, and special elements. Such a structure we call a *relational system*.

If we are interested in a particular relational system of this kind, we may construct a first-order language designed to convey information about it, as follows. First, we provide symbols to serve as names for each of the indicated operations, relations, and special elements of the system. Next, we include a list of symbols known as *individual variables,* which are interpreted to range over all of the elements of the given system. These variables, when used with "quantifier symbols" corresponding to the words "all" and "there is," permit us to make general and existential statements about the totality of elements of the rational system.

For example, in the case of the system of non-negative integers described above, which we shall call N, we can form such sentences as: "For all x and y, $x + y = y + x$"; or again, "there is a y, such that for all x, $y < x$." Finally, our language is provided with the sentential connectives (not, and, etc.) which occur in Post's system.

Of course, even though a language is created in this way for discussing a given relational system, there is nothing to prevent us from using exactly the same symbolism for discussing other relational systems, so that again we have the notion of a multiplicity of models for a given language. For example, in the case of the language designed to discuss the system N of non-negative integers, we could reinterpret the variables as ranging over all of the rational numbers (that is, the positive and negative fractions), the original symbols for addition and multiplication could be re-interpreted, respectively, as names for the operations of multiplication and subtraction on the rational numbers, the symbols for the relation *less than* and equality could have their meanings interchanged, as could the symbols 0 and 1.

Formal deductive theories based on such first-order languages were developed and studied by many logicians in the decade of the 1920's. Gödel's contribution was to show that one of these theories is logically complete, that is, that any sentence which is true in all models of the language is provable in this theory. Furthermore, Gödel's completeness theorem applies to a wide class of axiomatic theories which are based on first-order languages. For he showed that if one takes an *arbitrary* set of sentences of the language as new axioms, in addition to the logically valid axioms of the original deductive theory, and if one then considers the class C of all those models for which each of the new axioms is true, then every formula which is valid for C (that is, true for each model of C) will be provable in the enriched deductive system.

Gödel's proof of logical completeness differed from Post's in that it did not lead to a decision procedure for the class of logically valid first-order sentences. The problem whether such a procedure can be devised, that is, the decision problem for first-order logic, could not be resolved until the development of an important new concept—that of a recursive function—which will be discussed by S. C. Kleene in the next chapter.

Gödel's theorem, at the time of its publication in 1930, was viewed primarily as demonstrating the adequacy of the formal deductive method as a foundation for an important part of mathematics. Subsequent developments, however, showed it to have great value also as a tool in establishing various mathematical and metamathematical results. In these applications one generally employs a certain corollary of the completeness result which is known as the *compactness theorem*. This states that if we have an infinite list of first-order sentences, and if for each positive integer n one can find a model in which all of the first n sentences of the list are true, then one can find a single model for which all of the infinitely many sentences in the given list are true. The first application of this compactness theorem to a problem of abstract algebra was made by A. Malcev in 1941.

Post and Gödel were concerned primarily with logical completeness. In the decade which elapsed between their papers, several works were devoted to proofs of completeness with respect to single models. For example, in 1926, C. H. Langford considered the very simple relational system O consisting of the rational numbers with its ordering relation (no operations or special elements being considered). He provided a simple deductive theory based on the first-order language corresponding to this system, and was able to show that it is complete for O. A similar task was carried out by M. Presburger, in 1930, for the more complicated relational system consisting of the non-negative integers, the single operation of addition, the relation of equality, and the special elements 0 and 1. T. Skolem dealt similarly with the system whose sole operation was multiplication instead of addition.

In each of these cases where completeness with respect to a single model was established, the proof furnished a decision procedure for the class of provable sentences. Some years later, after the theory of recursive functions had been developed, this was understood to be far from coincidental. In terms of recursive functions, one can describe a broad class of formal deductive theories, of which one can say that whenever one of them is complete for a single model there must be a decision procedure for the class of its provable sentences.

The successive discoveries of completeness during the period 1919–30 encouraged many mathematicians to believe that in time the formal deductive method would prove a fully adequate basis for all mathematical theories. Thus it was that Gödel's paper of 1931, establishing that *incompleteness* characterized a very broad class of theories, came as a shock to the mathematical world and resulted in a fundamental shift in attitude toward the ultimate value of the formal deductive method.

Gödel dealt first with the phenomenon of incompleteness for theories of a single model; this was the system N of non-negative integers described above, in which both the operations of addition and multiplication are present. From these first results, he was then able to infer incompleteness for theories of various classes of models; in particular, many theories of logical validity were shown to be incomplete.

Among the theories which are incomplete for the model N are those based on the first-order language for this model. But Gödel achieved greater impact by first carrying out his incompleteness proof for another theory, which we shall call G, which is based on a language of higher order. This is obtained from the first-order one by adding new types of variables—for example, variables are provided which range over sets of integers, or over sets of sets of integers, along with the original variables ranging over the integers themselves. Thus, in the language of G we have sentences such as the following, which expresses the principle of mathematical induction: "If A is any set of non-negative integers which contains the number 0, and which along with any of its elements x also contains the next number, $x + 1$, then A contains all non-negative integers."

Axiomatic theories for the system of non-negative integers had been developed in the preceding century by Richard Dedekind and G. Peano. From their work, it was known that one can choose a set of axioms, including the principle of mathematical induction, with the property that *any* model which satisfies the axioms will be isomorphic to—that is, mathematically indistinguishable from—the system N itself. It is such an axiom set which appears in the deductive theory G. Because the axioms exclude models which differ mathematically from N, it was generally felt that the theory G must be complete for N. Yet Gödel showed that it was not.

Gödel's proof was compounded of two basic ideas, of which the first is that of *arithmetization*. This is the process, previously exploited so fruitfully in geometry, whereby numbers are attached to objects of some other domain, thereby providing for a reinterpretation of sentences which refer to numbers in their primary meaning. In particular by attaching numbers to the sentences of the theory G, Gödel is able to reinterpret this arithmetical language so that its sentences come to convey information about themselves.

The second basic idea of Gödel's proof is that of the Paradox of the Liar, which I mentioned in Chapter 2. Gödel was unable to find a sentence in the language of G which expresses the proposition that it itself is not true, but he was able to construct a sentence Q which asserts that it itself is *not provable in G*. If we assume Q were actually provable, it would therefore be false, hence both provable and false. But we know that all provable sentences are true. So Q cannot be provable. Since Q asserts that it is not provable, we see that Q is true. Thus we have a sentence which is true but not provable, so the theory G is incomplete.

An essential ingredient of this incompleteness proof is the demonstration that the notion *provable in G* can be expressed in the language of G itself. This possibility results from the fact that the rules of proof for G are of a very simple nature. But such simplicity of rules is essential to our notion of what a proof is, and to the purposes for which we use proofs. It thus appears that if G were strengthened by the addition of *any* acceptable rules of proof, the resulting deductive theory could still be shown incomplete by Gödel's method. To make these ideas mathematically precise the notion of a recursive function is needed; this will be explained by Professor Kleene in his chapter.

From his result that the theory G is incomplete for the model N, Gödel was able to obtain a very general incompleteness theorem. Namely, we consider *any* formal deductive theory *H*, based on a language of higher order, whose rules of proof are simple enough to be "acceptable." Then *H* is incomplete for *any* *class C* of models, as long as *C* contains at least one model whose domain is infinite. In particular, there cannot be a complete theory for the logically valid sentences of a higher order language.

To obtain this generalization, Gödel indicated a way of "translating" the unprovable sentences he had found for the theory *G* into the language of these other theories. By similar translation techniques, subsequent workers extended still further the scope of these incompleteness proofs.

Gödel's incompleteness results raised two problems.

First, having discovered that certain formal deductive systems are complete and others not, we can seek some general criterion for identifying complete theories—or, where such a criterion is lacking, we can examine individual theories of particular interest to determine whether they are complete.

Second, when we have at hand a particular formal deductive system *J*, which is known to be incomplete for a certain class *C* of models, the situation is that some sentences which are valid for *C* are provable in *J* while others are not. Accordingly, we may seek general criteria for distinguishing these two kinds of sentences.

Each of these types of problem has received attention in the period since 1931. Let us consider first the effort to sort the complete theories from the incomplete. Interest here has focused on formal deductive theories based on first-order languages, and on the question which of them is complete with respect to some single model *M*.

The most interesting case of this kind, found by Alfred Tarski, concerns the system *R* of real numbers with the usual operations for adding and multiplying them. (The real numbers are all those which are needed to express the distance between two points on a line.) The same first-order language which is used to convey facts about the system *N* of non-negative integers can be used to convey facts about R, simply by changing our interpretation of the range of the variables. For example, the sentence "There is a number x such that $x \cdot x = 2$" is false in the system N, but true in R. Although Gödel's results show that there is no deductive theory in which one can prove all the sentences of this language which are true in N, Tarski provided a deductive theory which he showed is capable of proving every sentence true in R.

Many other particular relational systems have been examined. For some, complete first-order deductive theories have been found, for others it has been shown that no such theories exist. We have no general criteria for distinguishing between these two kinds of relational systems.

On the other hand, instead of starting with a model and seeking a complete theory for it, we may start with a first-order deductive theory and ask the question whether there is some model for which it is complete. For this kind of problem we do have several general criteria which give us affirmative answers for a large class of deductive theories. However, the description of these criteria is too technical for inclusion in this essay.

Let us turn now to the second type of problem raised by Gödel's incompleteness results. Suppose we are given a deductive theory J whose theorems are all true in some model M, but which is not complete for M: How can we distinguish, among the sentences true in M, those which are provable in J from those which are not? In case J is based on a first-order language, Gödel's completeness theorem supplies an answer. If a sentence S is provable in J, it is true not only in M but in every model satisfying the axioms of J, while if S is unprovable it must be false for at least one of these models. However, if the language of J is of higher order, the situation is generally different.

For example, consider the higher-order theory G, employed by Gödel in his incompleteness proof, all of whose theorems are true in the system N of non-negative integers. We know there are other sentences true in N, which are not provable in G. However, such a sentence cannot be false in some other model which satisfies the axioms of G, for we have seen that any such model is mathematically indistinguishable from N.

33

The problem of sorting the provable from the unprovable, in higher-order theories, can be solved by enlarging the notion of *model*. For instance, in a second-order language we have one kind of variable ranging over elements of the domain of a model, and another kind ranging over sets of such elements, i.e., over subsets of the domain. Now by a *generalized model* for such a language we mean a model in the old sense, *together with* a chosen class of subsets of its domain. When we come to interpret the sentences of the language with respect to such a generalized model, we confine the set variables to range only over the chosen subsets of the domain, not over all subsets. For example, the axiom which expresses the principle of mathematical induction in Gödel's theory G would have the following meaning when interpreted with respect to a generalized model: If A is any *chosen* set of domain elements which contains the special element o, and if, whenever A contains an element x it also contains $x + 1$, then A contains *all* elements of the domain.

Because this axiom puts no restriction on the non-chosen sets of domain elements, it turns out that we can find generalized models satisfying the axioms of the theory G whose structure is very different from that of N. Furthermore, it can be shown that every sentence unprovable in G must be false for one of these models. In short, we obtain a completeness theorem for the theory G which is entirely analogous to Gödel's completeness result for first-order theories: G is complete for the class of all those generalized models which satisfy all of its axioms. And indeed, such a completeness theorem can be established not only for G, but for *arbitrary* theories of higher order.

This concludes our brief survey of the concept of completeness in modern studies of mathematical logic. We have observed that early completeness proofs were undertaken to justify the use of formal deductive theories as a foundation for mathematics. While Gödel's incompleteness results raised fundamental doubts on this score, they have served as a stimulus to further work in several directions. That we can hope to find significant examples of complete theories even among those which play a central role in mathematics is shown by Tarski's work on the theory of real numbers. The quest for general criteria by which to identify complete theories has led to several fruitful new metamathematical concepts. And in seeking a means of characterizing the class of provable sentences of an incomplete theory, we have been led to discover new mathematical structures and new ways of interpreting the language of mathematics.

4 COMPUTABILITY

S. C. Kleene

In Leon Henkin's chapter "Truth and Provability," we saw how the difficulties in investigating the *truth* of sentences directly from their meaning led mathematicians to substitute *provability*. The classical example is geometry as systematized by Euclid three centuries before Christ, using the axiomatic-deductive method, which is supposed to have been discovered by Pythagoras in the sixth century B.C. Only in the present century has this method finally been fully refined, so that the symbolism and syntax of the language employed, and the logical apparatus as well as the mathematical assumptions, are all explicitly specified. Thereby *axiomatic theories,* as exemplified by Euclid's geometry, became *formal deductive theories.*

Thus, formal deductive theories have arisen as the final refinement of using proofs to establish the truth of sentences under a presupposed interpretation of the language in terms of an object domain. In this refinement, the theories become so precise that they can be made the starting point of investigations, in which one can ask to what object domains a presupposed theory is applicable. Some of the remarkable results which have ensued from this reversal of the earlier point of view were touched upon in Professor Henkin's essay—"Completeness."

We shall in this chapter dwell upon the nature of the precision which has been achieved in formal deductive theories. Indeed, it consists in this: When an alleged proof in a given formal deductive theory is placed before a person, he can decide, *without* the necessity of any exercise of *ingenuity,* whether in fact it is a proof or not. He needs only to *verify* that it is constructed in conformity with the *rules* governing the construction of proofs (including the rules for the syntax of the language). These rules, for the given theory, were all to have been stated in advance, ready for direct application in a uniform and determinate manner.

The class of questions "Is this list of sentences a proof?" is a modern example of a class of questions, each question of which class can be answered without ingenuity by applying given rules. The rules, or procedure, for answering any question of such a class have been called an *algorithm,* after the corrupted name of the ninth-century Arabian mathematician al-Khuwarizme. But algorithms go back to the beginnings of mathematics. A trivial example is for the class of questions "Does the positive integer p divide the positive interger q?" An algorithm consists in performing the familiar process of dividing p by q, to obtain a quotient and a remainder; according as the remainder obtained is zero or greater than zero, the answer to the question is "yes" or "no." Besides algorithms for a class of *yes-or-no-questions,* one can have algorithms for *what-questions.* Thus, the example just given begins with the application of an algorithm for the question "What is the remainder when p is divided by q?"

Euclid's name is attached to an algorithm for finding the greatest common divisor of two positive integers p and q; and this algorithm is used in a further algorithm for answering the question "Does the linear equation $px + qy = r$ with the positive integral coefficients p, q and r have a solution for x and y in positive integers?" This is a less obvious algorithm than our first example. If we do not restrict the equations to be linear, but for example allow any algebraic equations, still with integral coefficients, no algorithm is known. Instead of *algorithm,* one often says *decision procedure* for yes-or-no-questions, and *computation procedure* for what-questions.

An algorithm always relates to a *class* of questions, and indeed an *infinite* class. The significant point is that one has a *finite* list of preassigned rules, or a *finitely* described procedure, the use of which will suffice for answering any one of the infinitely many questions. With a finite class of questions, the situation is trivial:

the rules can simply enumerate the answers to each of the questions.

Despite the fact that over 2,000 years of mathematical history are studded with *examples* of algorithms, it was not until the decade 1930–40 that the *general concept* of an algorithm was properly analyzed. The impetus for this analysis came from the prominence the concept received in connection with formal deductive theories. Once it was recognized that the essential achievement of a formal deductive theory is to establish an algorithm for the question "Is this list of sentences a proof?" people could not help but wonder whether their objective in setting up the theory could not be achieved more directly by finding an algorithm for the question "Is this sentence provable?" The problem of finding an algorithm for the latter class has come to be called *the decision problem* for the theory. If a formal deductive theory could be established complete for some significant domain of mathematics, and the decision problem for it could be solved affirmatively, then, at least theoretically if not practically, we would have a touchstone for all mathematical knowledge concerning that domain.

Let us now adopt the mathematical terminology of *functions*. When we have a class of what-questions, posed by giving numbers, for example two non-negative integers p and q, and to be answered by giving a unique number r, mathematicians say that r is a *function* of p and q. Our problem is, for which functions of p and q (or of other lists of variables) are there algorithms? Yes-or-no-questions can be included as a special case of what-questions by using 0 for *yes* and 1 for *no*.

The analysis of the general concept of algorithm in the 1930's was achieved by identifying the class of all the functions for which there are algorithms in the intuitive and historical sense with a certain mathematically described class of functions. In fact, three principal different mathematical descriptions of a class of functions emerged in their period, which, either through the properties the class was found to have or from the way it was described, became candidates for this role.

These were the so-called *lambda-definable functions* studied by A. Church and Kleene in 1932 and and 1933; the *general recur-*

sive functions described by Gödel in 1934 building on a suggestion of J. Herbrand; and the *computable functions* characterized independently by A. M. Turing and by E. L. Post in 1936. These three differently described classes were proved to comprise exactly the same functions. Church first, and Turing and Post shortly thereafter, made the claim that they are all (and only) the functions for which there are algorithms. Three of the six persons just mentioned were Americans, Gödel was Austrian but soon settled in America, while Herbrand was French and Turing was English.

The plausibility of this claim, which we call *Church's thesis* or the *Church-Turing thesis* (and its converse), lies nearest the surface in the case of Turing's computable functions; so we use these for our remaining remarks. In the literature, the general recursive functions have been used more often.

When Turing first wrote, the public was less aware than now of digital computers. Turing's and the other mathematical formulations and studies of the notion of all functions computable by algorithms had a close relation to the recent rapid evolution of actual digital computers. Turing himself and other logicians became involved in computing laboratories.

Taking the notion of a physical digital computer as familiar now, the theoretical concept of a computable function is easily reached. We simply divest the physical machines of their practical limitations.

First, we assume machines that never make any errors; that is, that obey the intended laws for their action without any deviation.

The next idealization is connected with the fact that an algorithm relates to an infinite class of questions; for example, the question "What is the value r of a certain function for the values p and q of its variables?" where p and q range over all pairs of non-negative integers. Not even in the simplest cases, such as when $r = p + q$, can a physical machine compute r for every p and q. With very large p and q, there will not be sufficient capacity in the machine for it even to receive the inputs p and q. Theoretically, we deal with this by separating the machine proper, which does the computing and thus determines

39

what function will be computed, from the peripheral information storage facility, in which the p and q are given to the machine, in which the machine can keep its scratchwork (that is, store information required at intermediate stages of the computation), and in which the machine can deliver the answer r. The machine proper represents the finite list of rules in our intuitive description of an algorithm.

Proceeding to details, we may consider equally spaced *moments* of time, numbered 0, 1, 2, ... At each moment, the *machine* shall be in one of a *finite* number of possible *states*. The peripheral facility can be an infinite linear *tape* divided into *squares,* and passing through the machine so that at each moment one square is *scanned* by the machine. Each square of the tape may at each moment be *blank* or have printed upon it any one of a finite number of possible configurations of symbols, or, by redefinition of the symbols, any one of a finite number of *symbols*. We arrange that at any moment only finitely much information be on the tape by requiring that all but a finite number of the squares be blank.

However, there can be no finite upper bound to this number, since we aim to use the machine to compute a function of p and q for all values of p and q. Between a given moment and the next, the machine can erase and/or print any of the admissible symbols on the scanned square; it can shift its scanning position on the tape one square leftward or rightward (or neither); and it can alter its own state. This composite action of the machine between a given moment and the next shall be completely determined by the state of the machine and of the scanned tape-square at the given moment. Mathematically, a *Turing machine* is then nothing more than a finite table describing this action for each of the finitely many machine states and scanned tape-square states possible for the machine. Finally, you can surely figure out a system for presenting the values of p and q to the machine on the tape at the moment 0 with the machine in a specified state, and for receiving the resulting value r of the function on the tape at some moment t; the moment t when r is received can be signaled by the machine's first assuming another specified state. A function of p and q is *Turing computable,* if there is a Turing machine which thus computes its value r for each pair of values of p and q.

According to the Church-Turing thesis, any function for which intuitively there is an algorithm, or as we may say is "computable" in the intuitive sense, is computable by a Turing machine as just described.

Now that we have an exact delineation of the totality of computable functions, we can ask, and for the first time we can hope to answer, the question whether all functions are in principle computable. Here, for simplicity, we deal with functions of only one variable p.

We recall that mathematically any particular Turing machine is fully characterized by a finite table determining the action it performs between one moment and the next. Such a table can be converted into a "code number." For example, if the table be typed out on my typewriter, which has 82 individual symbols including the space (more than we really need), these symbols could be replaced by the two-digit combinations 01, 02, 03, . . . , 82. Thereby the table would become just monstrous number, which we call the *code number* of the machine.

Now we describe a function which we shall see is not computable; call it *our* function. Consider any value of p. We ask two questions successively. (1) Is p the code number of a Turing machine? (2) If so, will that machine, if it is applied to compute a function for p as value of the variable, actually produce a value q? If the answers to both questions are "yes," we let $q + 1$ (for the q in the answer to Question (2)) be the value of our function corresponding to p. Otherwise, we let o be the value of our function corresponding to p.

Now we show that our function is not computable. Suppose it were computable. Then some Turing machine M would compute it for all values of p. This machine would have a code number c. When we consider c as value of p, we get contradictory results. Say the machine M applied to c computes the value q; this is the value of our function because M computes our function. But on the other hand, with Questions (1) and (2) both answered in the affirmative for $p = c$, the value of our function is $q + 1$ by definition. This value can't be both q and $q + 1$. So our supposition was wrong; our function is not computable.

Examples of this sort given in 1936 by Church, by Turing and by Kleene opened up a new area of research. Expressed in other words, we have found a class of questions for which there can be no algorithm. Of course the questions are not ones anyone would have thought of asking before; as mathematicians sometimes say, we have constructed a "pathological example." But it leads to other examples, in some of which the questions are ones logicians or other mathematicians were already asking.

Let us reconsider the definition of our uncomputable function, and ask ourselves why we can't compute it simply by applying our definition of it. A little reflection will show that we could, except for only one difficulty. This comes in trying to answer Question (2). Let R be the binary relation between two numbers p and t which holds true exactly in the following case: the first number p is the code number of a Turing machine, and this machine, if applied to compute for p as value of the variable, will at the moment t first produce a value q. Write this: $p \, R \, t$.

Using the relation R, Question (2) can be stated thus: Does a number t exist such that $p \, R \, t$? There can be no algorithm for Question (2), or there would be an algorithm for the whole, which we know there isn't. The relation $p \, R \, t$ is in fact computable. A detailed investigation would be required to describe explicitly a Turing machine that computes it. However, an algorithm for it is immediate, since we can test p for compatibility with the requirements for being the code number of a machine, and if p is, then we can imitate the action of that machine applied to p up to the given moment t. Thus we have discovered that there is an uncomputable (or undecidable) property having the form "there exists a t such that $p \, R \, t$," where $p \, R \, t$ is a computable relation.

Consider this property further. When a number p has this property, we can intuitively "prove" that fact as follows: Pick the right t, and show that $p \, R \, t$ is true by computation.

Consider any formal deductive theory, call it N, which is adequate for simple mathematics on the level of elementary number theory, also called arithmetic. In the theory N, we should be able to express the aforementioned property for particular numbers p by respective sentences of the theory, a different sentence, call it S_p, for each value of p. Furthermore, when a number p has the property, the intuitive proof that it has should have as counterpart a proof in the formal deductive theory of the corresponding sentence S_p. Let us further suppose that, in the theory N, sentences are only provable when they are true under the usual interpretation of the language of N. Then S_p is provable in N exactly when there exists a t such that $p\ R\ t$.

Since the property that there exists a t such that $p\ R\ t$ is undecidable, it follows that the decision problem for the theory N cannot be solved affirmatively; that is, there can be no algorithm to answer the question "Is this sentence provable in N?" The formal deductive theory N for which we have this result is any which is adequate and correct for some intuitive elementary number theory. Thus the dream of a touchstone for all mathematical knowledge at this level is shown to be unattainable.

Careful study shows that the sentences S_p, and their proofs when true, can be paraphrased in the theory of first-order predicate logic, call it L. So the undecidability result applies already to L, as Church and Turing each showed in 1936.

For the case of the theory N, we can also conclude incompleteness. For, suppose N were complete. Then, for each number p, the sentence S_p or the sentence expressing the contrary, call it not-S_p, but not both, would be provable in N. So we could decide whether or not there exists a t such that $p\ R\ t$ by searching through the provable sentences of N until we first encounter S_p or not-S_p. This would contradict the undecidability of the property that there exists a t such that $p\ R\ t$. Thus we have established the famous incompleteness theorem of Gödel on the basis of purely structural aspects of a formal deductive theory, plus only the adequacy of the theory N and its correctness for some elementary number-theoretic reasoning. By the structural aspects, we can test whether any list of sentences is a proof, and thus by testing all such lists and rejecting those which fail the test, we can search through all the provable sentences. There is, therefore, no escape from the Gödel incompleteness. It results from the very features of formal deductive theories for which they were

43

devised. Here, for brevity, we have used an indirect argument; a little further investigation would show how we can actually find a p for which not-S_p is unprovable in N though true under the usual interpretation.

To summarize: analysis of the notion of a formal deductive theory led to that of algorithms or computability in general, and thence to the discovery of uncomputable functions and properties. These are so simple that they entail the undecidability and incompleteness of any formal deductive theory N embracing (and correct for) a modicum of elementary intuitive number theory.

In conclusion, we shall indicate three further developments made possible by the general analysis of algorithms.

Starting with the work of Kleene, of A. Mostowski in Poland, and of Post, a whole hierarchy of "degrees" of uncomputability has been discovered. For example, we can consider properties of the form that, for all s, there exists a t, such that some computable ternary relation holds between p, s and t. A suitably chosen property K of this form is not computable, nor is it expressible in the form that there exists a t such that p bears a computable relation to t. It is *more* uncomputable than any property L of the latter form, in the following sense.

Consider a machine like a Turing machine, except that it has access to an infinite tape, listing the answers to all the questions whether p has the property L. No such machine can, for each p, compute whether p has the property K. But a suitable machine with access to all answers whether p has the property K can answer all questions whether p has the property L. The system of the degrees of uncomputability which exist among the properties of non-negative integers possesses an unexpectedly complicated structure.

A. Tarski, Mostowski, and others have established the undecidability of a variety of formal deductive theories based on first-order predicate logic with various sets of mathematical axioms, such as for algebraic systems. Examples of such theories which are decidable were mentioned by Professor Henkin in Chapter 3.

Finally, Post, Turing, and in the U.S.S.R. A. A. Markov and P. S. Novikov, and others, have demonstrated the impossibility of the existence of some algorithms which mathematicians have been seeking in branches of mathematics apart from logic, especially in algebra and recently in topology; for example, to determine whether two descriptions of elements of a system by different combinations of basic elements describe in fact the same element.

The impossibility, of course, rests on the Church-Turing thesis, which is accepted by most workers in the foundations of mathematics. For the few who remain skeptics, it is shown by such results that an algorithm would have to be one which could not be mechanized by a Turing machine. When it is understood that by an "algorithm" we mean a fully determinate process using only finitely many preassigned rules in a uniform manner, none of the skeptics has given a plausible suggestion of what an algorithm which would not be mechanizable in Turing's manner could be like.

5 NECESSARY TRUTH

Willard V. Quine

If people thought that very little of what went on in the world happened by necessity, then surely they would have little occasion to use the adverb "necessarily." But the adverb is in fact frequently heard. So people must think that quite a lot happens by necessity.

But if people thought that almost everything that happened at all happened by necessity, then again they would have little occasion to use the adverb "necessarily"; mostly it would go without saying. So people must think that while much of what goes on happens by necessity, much of it also does not. People must have some criterion which they keep using to sort the passing states and events into some that happened with necessity and others that happened without necessity. Otherwise the adverb "necessarily" would not be heard so often. Or so it would seem.

Actually, of course, this is wrong. People have no such criterion. They would be hard put to it to classify any of the passing events outright as necessary or otherwise. For the fact is that the adverb "necessarily," as it is most often used, does not mark a present or past event or state outright as necessary.

Future ones, yes; often we represent a future event or state as necessary or not, according as we have or have not good reason to expect it. We say, "Surely she will worry"; that is, necessarily. We say, "The inhabitants are bound to be hostile"; they will necessarily be hostile. We ask, "Will it break?" and are told, "Not necessarily."

I have had to allow in these examples for a certain vernacular twist: generally "necessarily" sounds well after a "not" or "then," whereas such synonyms as "surely" and "bound to" and "must" are often preferred elsewhere.

These necessity idioms are not indeed confined to the future. But when they enter the present and past, they still tend to connote conjecture or inference: thus "As mayor he must have enriched himself"—necessarily did—"for look at his earlier record on the school board." It is paradoxical that these strong words, "necessarily" and its synonyms, are used mainly where we are less than sure of the facts. What we really know we usually just affirm, without the intensive.

Should we in general dismiss the adverb "necessarily," then, as a mere rhetorical device that people use to cover their uncertainty? No, there is a case for another account. To make it I shall turn to a more trivial example. Someone says, "Surely it has spots," "Necessarily it will have spots," when told that he is about to be shown a leopard. Now, instead of viewing the adverb "necessarily" as governing outright the simple prediction of spots, we can understand it as governing, implicitly, the conditional sentence as a whole: "If it is a leopard, it has spots." In attributing a quality of necessity to this whole conditional compound, there is no air of paradox, certainly, nor of rhetorical subterfuge.

Something of the same may be done for the other future-tense examples. When we say, "The inhabitants are bound to be hostile," we are basing our prediction on something—perhaps the recent burning of their granary. So, instead of associating the necessity with the inhabitants' hostility outright, we can understand it as attaching to the conditional sentence as a whole: "Necessarily, if their granary was lately burned, the inhabitants will be hostile." Again, when we ask, "Will it break?" we mean, "If I use it, will it break?" so the reassuring answer, "Not necessarily," can be seen as applying not to the mere breaking but to the conditional sentence as a whole, as if to say, "It is not necessarily true that if you use it it will break."

This treatment works not only for the future-tense examples but also, of course, for the conjectures regarding the present and past. "As mayor he must have enriched himself": we may take the necessity as applying not to this conjectured self-enrichment

47

as such, but to the whole implicit conditional, "If when on the school board he did thus and so, then also as mayor he will have enriched himself."

In a word the point is, in all cases, to seek the necessity not in the separate matters of fact but in the connections between them. No wonder people would be hard put to it to classify passing events as necessary or otherwise; it is a question rather of connections.

The next question is, "What does it take to qualify a connection as necessary?" Here we do well to return again to our trivial example of the leopard. Some leopard is announced, and we expect spots; what is the connection? Clearly, a generality: *all* leopards have spots.

In this I think there is the germ of an explanation of the less trivial examples as well. I submit that whenever one says, "Necessarily if *p* then *q*," he has at least dimly in mind some fairly dependable generalization under which his particular "if *p* then *q*" can be subsumed as a case. The leopard example is trivial only because there the relevant generalization is so easily recognized: Why should this newly heralded leopard necessarily have spots? Because they all have spots. Other examples, such as the one about the hostility of the natives, differ from the leopard example only in that the relevant generalization is less clearly hinted in the phrasing of the sentences. "Always or usually, when you burn their granary, people turn hostile"; the speaker is bound to have had some such generality in mind, and this it is that lends the force to his "necessarily" when he says of his particular instance that necessarily, if *their* granary was lately burned, *these* inhabitants will be hostile.

A cautionary remark of a rather subtle kind is called for at this point. We must not suppose that a man is entitled to apply "necessarily" to an assertion so long merely as he thinks there is *some* general truth that subsumes it. Thus, suppose I have lost my key. Then immediately we have this trivial generalization: It is true of everyone *x* without exception that if *x* is I, *x* lost his key. Just as on the strength of all leopards having spots we say that necessarily the upcoming leopard will have spots, so on the strength of this new generalization we might expect to be able to say that necessarily, I being indeed I, I lost my key. This line would allow us to attribute necessity to anything, however casual, that we are prepared to affirm at all.

I am therefore not suggesting that "Necessarily if p then q" can be defined to mean "There is a true generalization whereof an instance is that if p then q." It is a matter rather of the speaker's having antecedently in mind some one actual generalization whose truth is, in his view, independent of particulars of the case in hand. It is this feeling, I suggest, that would normally prompt the speaker to attach "Necessarily" to his "if p then q." He might rather have attached "So, in particular" if his antecedent generalization had actually been antecedently spoken.

What I have done thus far may be summed up as two steps. First, I have argued that the adverb "necessarily" applies only by ellipsis to particular events or states, and properly rather to whole conditional connections: "Necessarily if p then q." Second, I have presented this "necessarily" in turn, the "necessarily" of "Necessarily if p then q," simply as an allusion to some presently more or less hinted regularity, "All A are B," which subsumes the particular link "if p then q" as a case.

The doctrine that necessity is no more than regularity was expounded by David Hume more than two centuries ago. His, indeed, was the battle cry, "There are no necessary connections of matters of fact." He meant, of course, that there are none if "necessary" is taken as claiming more than generality, or regularity. I am not taking it as claiming more.

One place in the philosophy of science where the idea of necessity comes in for special attention is in analyzing the so-called disposition terms, such as "soluble." To say of a particular lump of stuff that it is soluble in water is, as Rudolf Carnap has stressed, to say more about it than just that whenever it is in water it dissolves. For perhaps this particular lump will never be in water. By default, then, even if the lump is quartz, it would be true that whenever the lump is in water it dissolves; but we cannot on that ground call it soluble in water. For a lump to be soluble we must be able to say of it that if it *were* in water it *would* dissolve; we need an "if-then" connection governed by necessity, and by a necessity that goes beyond mere generality

NECESSARY TRUTH

over time. To say merely that the lump dissolves each time
that it *is* in water is too weak.

Advances in chemistry eventually redeem the solubility idea,
but only in terms of a full-blown theory. We come to understand
just what there is about the submicroscopic form and composition of a solid that enables water to dissolve it. Thenceforward,
solubility can simply be equated to these explanatory traits.
When we say of a lump that it would necessarily dissolve if in
water, we can be understood as attributing to the lump those sup-
posedly enumerated details of submicroscopic structure—those
explanatory traits with which we are imagining solubility to have
been newly equated. A chemist can tell you what they are. I
cannot.

Surely, it will be felt, something is wrong here. I seem to be
talking intelligibly of solubility, yet by this account it is only the
chemist, and neither you nor I, who knows its defining traits.
Moreover, the term was already used just as freely and easily
before even the chemists had arrived at those explanatory traits.

Still, I think we are on the right track. Early and late, solubility has been meant to be some causal agency or mechanism or
arrangement in the lump, however little understood. From the
start of a scientific attitude anyway, the term has been a sort of
promissory note which one might hope eventually to redeem in
terms of an explicit account of the working mechanism. What
kind of account of a mechanism might pass as explanatory depends somewhat, of course, upon the general situation in science
at the time. Nowadays, in general, one settles for an account in
terms of the arrangement and movement of molecules, or of
smaller particles when finer texture is relevant.

And meanwhile the promissory character of the unredeemed
solubility idea was never an obstacle to glib use of the term. For
this much one is assured of early and late: whenever a soluble
thing is in water it does dissolve. We intend in advance that
solubility consist precisely in those explanatory traits of structure and composition, however ill pictured or unpictured at the
moment, that do make things dissolve when in water.

A disposition term that contrasts interestingly with "soluble" is
"intelligent." Solubility is the capacity to dissolve in water; in-

telligence is the capacity to learn, or to solve problems. Whereas chemists have redeemed the solubility idea by uncovering the explanatory traits, the intelligence idea is still as unredeemed as can be. We do not even know whether to seek the explanatory traits in the chemistry of the nerve cells, or in the topology of the nerve net, or in both, or somewhere else. Intelligence today is where solubility was centuries ago. Still I think it is a promissory note. I do not think we would use the word "intelligent" if we did not think there was an unidentified but some day identifiable causal agency or mechanism that sets one man above another in learning and in the solving of problems.

This account of disposition terms is not to deny that "x is soluble" means that if x were in water, it would dissolve. This equation is still good. Accordingly what I proceeded to say about disposition terms serves, in so far as it illuminates them, to illuminate also the subjunctive conditional idiom itself: "If x were treated thus and so, it would do such and such." This even is the general idiom for attributing dispositions; whether a single word like "soluble" or "intelligent" happens also to exist for the disposition is immaterial.

In general, when we say "If x were treated thus and so, it would do such and such," we are attributing to x some theoretical explanatory trait or cluster of traits. Typically these would be traits of microscopic structure or substance. Sometimes they are analytically describable in all explicitness, by specialists if not by us, as in the case of solubility. Sometimes they are envisioned only as some day describable.

Such a conditional sentence may or may not flaunt the adverb "necessarily"; in any event the subjunctive form connotes it. Now, altogether, the uses of the necessary conditional are varied and unsystematic. But this use, for imputing dispositions, is an important one among them.

Another use was seen in the example of the leopard and the spots, which so neatly fitted Hume's theory of necessity as generality. Now the conditional as used to impute dispositions may be said, in a sense, to come under Hume's theory too. If this lump were in water, it would dissolve; where is the underlying generality? It is in the explanatory trait, which is solubility itself:

everything that has that subtle trait of microstructure dissolves when in water.

In each of the necessity constructions, even the leopard example, the speaker has some one line of generalization in mind and not another. In the leopard example we easily guess: it is a question of all leopards. In the example of the inhabitants' being hostile we could not guess, but had to be told that the speaker was generalizing over people whose granaries were burned. And, in the necessity constructions that impute dispositions, the generality lies along some known or posited explanatory trait.

Thus, the necessity constructions that impute dispositions do not depart from the Humean pattern. They turn, still, on generality. But they turn on theory, too, precisely because they fix upon explanatory traits for their domains of generality.

The uses of "necessarily" that we have been considering up to now might loosely be spoken of as physical or natural necessity, as against the narrower notion of *logical* or *mathematical* necessity. A truth that might be cited under this latter category is that momentum is proportional to velocity. This might be said to be logically or mathematically necessary on the ground that the word "momentum" is itself defined simply as short for "mass times velocity."

But now imagine a physicist with some unexpected experimental findings to provide for. They conflict with his physical theory. There is no specific point in his theory that they conflict with, for observations do not conflict with theoretical statements one by one. But they show that the theory taken conjunctively is false, and must be changed at one point or another to inactivate the false prediction. And now suppose the physicist hits upon a particularly neat repair, which involves revising slightly the law that momentum is proportional to velocity: he makes momentum proportional instead to, say, velocity divided by one minus the reciprocal of the square of the speed of light, which deviates negligibly for most purposes.

Will his colleagues protest that he is flying in the face of logical necessity? Will they protest that he is departing from the definition of "momentum" and so depriving his theory of meaning? Will they protest that he is redefining momentum and so merely playing with words? I think they will do none of these things. His modification of the proportionality of momentum to velocity will strike them in no other way than a modification of any other time-honored proposition of physics might strike them. And this, I feel, is as it should be.

In supposing the contrary, we unduly exalt the act of definition. There are two ways in which we may learn a theoretical term: through context, by learning a network of laws in which the term occurs; and through definition, by learning what phrase to substitute the term for. But this difference may best be seen merely as a difference in the history of one's learning, and not as making for an enduring difference in status between the variously interlocking laws of the theory itself.

Thus I am inclined to dismiss the idea that a special category of necessity, the logical or mathematical, is represented by the law that momentum is proportional to velocity. And my reason is that I attach no relevance to the status of definition.

The statement that momentum is proportional to velocity was supposed to be mathematically necessary because that definition, when expanded, turned the statement into a mathematical triviality. It may be well, then, if my skepticism is over the definition, to forget the definition and turn our attention to the mathematical triviality itself: "Mass times velocity is proportional to velocity." How is *this* for a case of mathematical necessity?

Admirable, certainly. But is even this necessity somehow different in kind from what can be attributed to ordinary truths of physical theory or other natural sciences? A long-standing doctrine says that it is; and I should like to conclude by questioning that doctrine. It depends, I think, upon a terminological boundary between physics and mathematics.

Thus let us begin by supposing that we have somehow drawn a boundary across the face of physics, at some points perhaps quite arbitrary, so as to separate a more speculative and theoretical half of physics from a more experimental and empirical half. Let us call the one side theoretical physics and the other experimental physics. Now it strikes me that the contrasts that people are prone to draw between pure mathematics such as arithmetic, on the one hand, and physics on the other, can be drawn just as well between theoretical physics and experimental physics.

People say that physics is about the world, that it has empirical content, while arithmetic and other parts of pure mathematics do not. They grant that these mathematical disciplines have their motivation and their utility in the applications to physics and other natural sciences, but they call this a matter of motivation and application only, not of content. Now why can we not say precisely this of theoretical physics in relation to experimental? Certainly it has its motivation and utility in applications to experimental physics, but why not say that this again is a matter of motivation only, not of content? I think our not saying this is an accident of nomenclature. Theoretical and experimental physics are both called physics; we see them as part of a single systematic enterprise, connecting ultimately with observation. Pure mathematics, on the other hand, partly because of its additional utility in natural sciences other than physics, is segregated in name; so we do not see it as just a further part of a broader systematic enterprise, still connecting ultimately with the observations of experimental physics and other natural sciences.

Boundaries between disciplines are useful for deans and librarians, but let us not overestimate them—the boundaries. When we abstract from them, we see all of science—physics, biology, economics, mathematics, logic, and the rest—as a single sprawling system, loosely connected in some portions but disconnected nowhere. Parts of it—logic, arithmetic, game theory, theoretical parts of physics—are farther from the observational or experimental edge than other parts. But the overall system, with all its parts, derives its aggregate empirical content from that edge; and the theoretical parts are good only as they contribute in their varying degrees of indirectness to the systematizing of that content.

In principle, therefore, I see no higher or more austere necessity than natural necessity; and in natural necessity, or our attributions of it, I see only Hume's regularities, culminating here and there in what passes for an explanatory trait or the promise of it.

6 WHAT IS A SCIENTIFIC THEORY?

Patrick Suppes

Often when we ask what is a so-and-so, we expect a clear and definite answer. If, for example, someone asks me what is a rational number, I may give the simple and precise answer that a rational number is the ratio of two integers. There are other kinds of simple questions for which a precise answer can be given but for which in ordinary talk a rather vague answer is usually given and accepted. Someone reads about nectarines in a book, but has never seen a nectarine, or possibly has seen nectarines but is not familiar with their English name. He may ask me, "What is a nectarine?" and I would probably reply, "A smooth-skinned sort of peach." Certainly, this is not a very exact answer, but if my questioner knows what peaches are, it may come close to being satisfactory.

The kind of question I want to discuss fits neither one of these patterns. Scientific theories are not like rational numbers or nectarines. Certainly they are not like nectarines, for they are not simple physical objects. They are like rational numbers in not being physical objects, but they are totally unlike rational numbers in that scientific theories cannot be defined in any simple or direct way in terms of other non-physical, abstract objects.

Good examples of the kind of question we shall analyze in this chapter are provided by the familiar inquiries: "What is physics?," "What is psychology?," "What is science?" To none of these questions do we expect a simple and precise answer. On the other hand, there are many interesting things to be said

55

about the sort of thing physics or psychology is. I shall be trying to show in this essay that this is also true of scientific theories.

THE STANDARD SKETCH

The standard sketch of scientific theories—and I emphasize the word "sketch"—runs something like the following. A scientific theory consists of two parts. One part is an abstract logical calculus. In addition to the vocabulary of logic, this calculus includes the primitive symbols of the theory, and the logical structure of the theory is fixed by stating the axioms or postulates of the theory in terms of its primitive symbols. For many theories the primitive symbols will be thought of as theoretical terms like "electron" or "particle" that are not possible to relate in any simple way to observable phenomena.

The second part of the theory is a set of rules that assign an empirical content to the logical calculus by providing what are usually called "co-ordinating definitions" or "empirical interpretations" for at least some of the primitive and defined symbols of the calculus. It is always emphasized that the first part alone is not sufficient to define a scientific theory, for without a systematic specification of the intended empirical interpretation of the theory, it is not possible in any sense to evaluate the theory as a part of science, although it can be studied simply as a piece of pure mathematics.

The most striking thing about this characterization is its highly schematic nature. Concerning the first part of a theory, the logical calculus, it is unheard of to find a substantive example of a theory actually worked out as a logical calculus in the writings of most philosophers of science. Much handwaving is indulged in to demonstrate that this working out of the logical calculus is simple in principle and only a matter of tedious detail, but concrete evidence is seldom given.

The sketch of the second part of a theory, that is, the co-ordinating definitions or empirical interpretations of some of the terms, is also highly schematic. A common defense of the relatively vague schema offered is that the variety of different empirical interpretations, for example, the many different methods of measuring mass—make a precise characterization difficult. Moreover, as we move from the precisely formulated theory on to the very loose and elliptical sort of experimental language used by almost all scientists, it is difficult to impose a definite pattern on the rules of empirical interpretation.

The view I want to support in this essay is not that this standard sketch is wrong, but rather that it is far too simple. Its very sketchiness makes it possible to omit both important properties of theories and significant distinctions that may be introduced between different theories.

MODELS VERSUS EMPIRICAL INTERPRETATIONS

To begin with, there has been a strong tendency on the part of many philosophers to speak of the first part of a theory as a logical calculus purely in syntactical terms. The co-ordinating definitions provided in the second part do not in the sense of modern logic provide an adequate semantics for the formal calculus. Quite apart from questions about direct empirical observations, it is pertinent and natural from a logical standpoint to talk about the models of the theory. These models are highly abstract, non-linguistic entities, often quite remote in their conception from empirical observations. It may well be asked what does the concept of a model have to add to the familiar discussions of empirical interpretation of theories.

I think it is true to say that most philosophers find it easier to talk about theories than about models of theories. The reasons for this are several, but perhaps the most important two are the following: In the first place, philosophers' examples of theories are usually quite simple in character, and therefore are easy to discuss in a straightforward linguistic manner. In the second place, the introduction of models of a theory inevitably introduces a stronger mathematical element into the discussion. It is a natural thing to talk about theories as linguistic entities—that is, to speak explicitly of the precisely defined set of sentences of

57

the theory and the like—when the theories are given in what is called standard formalization.

Theories are ordinarily said to have a standard formalization when they are formulated within first-order logic. Roughly speaking, first-order logic is just the logic of sentential connectives and predicates holding for one type of object. Unfortunately, when a theory assumes more than first-order logic, it is neither natural nor simple to formalize it in this fashion. For example, if in axiomatizing geometry, we want to define lines as certain *sets* of points, we must work within a framework that already includes the ideas of set theory. To be sure, it is theoretically possible to axiomatize simultaneously geometry *and* the relevant portions of set theory, but this is awkward and unduly laborious.

Theories of more complicated structure like quantum mechanics, classical thermodynamics, or a modern quantitative version of learning theory, need to use not only general ideas of set theory but also many results concerning the real numbers. Formalization of such theories in first-order logic is utterly impractical. Theories of this sort are similar to the theories mainly studied in pure mathematics in their degree of complexity. In such contexts it is very much simpler to assert things about models of the theory rather than to talk directly and explicitly about the sentences of the theory, perhaps the main reason for this being that the notion of a sentence of the theory is not well defined when the theory is not given in standard formalization.

I would like to give just two examples in which the notion of model enters in a natural and explicit way in discussing scientific theories. The first example is concerned with the nature of measurement. The primary aim of a given theory of measurement is to show in a precise fashion how to pass from qualitative observations to the quantitative assertions needed for more elaborate theoretical stages of science. An analysis of how this passage from the qualitative to the quantitative may be performed is provided by axiomatizing appropriate algebras of experimentally realizable operations and relations. Given an axiomatized theory of measurement of some empirical quantity such as mass, distance, or force, the mathematical task is to prove a representation theorem for *models* of the theory which establishes, roughly speaking, that any empirical model is isomorphic to some numerical model of the theory. The existence of this isomorphism between models justifies the application of numbers to things.

We cannot literally take a number in our hands and apply it to a physical object. What we can do is to show that the structure of a set of phenomena under certain empirical operations is the same as the structure of some set of numbers under arithmetical operations and relations. The definition of isomorphism of models in the given context makes the intuitive idea of *same structure* precise. The great significance of finding such an isomorphism of models is that we may then use all our familiar knowledge of computational methods, as applied to the arithmetical model, to infer facts about the isomorphic empirical model. A linguistic formulation of this central notion of an empirical model of a theory of measurement being isomorphic to a numerical model is extremely awkward and tedious to formulate. But in model-theoretic terms the notion is simple and in fact represents a direct application of the very general notion of isomorphism used throughout all domains of pure mathematics.

The second example of the use of models concerns the discussion of reductionism in the philosophy of science. Many of the problems formulated in connection with the question of reducing one science to another may be formulated as a series of problems using the notion of a representation theorem for the models of a theory. For instance, the thesis that psychology may be reduced to physiology would be for many people appropriately established if one could show that for any model of a psychological theory it was possible to construct an isomorphic model within physiological theory.

The absence at the present time of any deep unitary theory within either psychology or physiology makes present attempts to settle such a question of reductionism rather hopeless. The classical example from physics is the reduction of thermodynamics to statistical mechanics. Although this reduction is usually not stated in absolutely satisfactory form from a logical standpoint, there is no doubt that it is substantially correct and represents one of the great triumphs of mathematical physics.

59

INTRINSIC VERSUS EXTRINSIC CHARACTERIZATION

Quite apart from the two applications just mentioned of the concept of a model of a theory, we may bring this concept to bear directly on the question of characterizing a scientific theory. The contrast I wish to draw is between intrinsic and extrinsic characterization. The formulation of a theory as a logical calculus or, to put it in terms that I prefer, as a theory with a standard formalization, gives an intrinsic characterization, but this is certainly not the only approach. For instance, a natural question to ask within the context of logic is if a certain theory *can* be axiomatized with standard formalization, that is, within first-order logic. In order to formulate such a question in a precise manner, it is necessary to have some extrinsic way of characterizing the theory. One of the simplest ways of providing such an extrinsic characterization is simply to define the intended class of models of the theory. To ask if we can axiomatize the theory is then just to ask if we can state a set of axioms such that the models of these axioms are precisely the models in the defined class.

As a very simple example of a theory formulated both extrinsically and intrinsically, consider the extrinsic formulation of the theory of simple orderings that are isomorphic to a set of real numbers under the familiar less-than relation. That is, consider the class of all binary relations isomorphic to some fragment of the less-than relation for the real numbers. The extrinsic characterization of a theory usually follows the sort given for these orderings: namely, we designate a particular model of the theory (in this case, the numerical less-than relation) and then characterize the entire class of models of the theory in relation to this distinguished model.

The problem of intrinsic characterization is now to formulate a set of axioms that will characterize this class of models without referring to the relation between models, but only to the intrinsic properties of any one model. With the present case the solution is relatively simple, although even it is not easily formulated within first-order logic. The intrinsic axioms are just those for a simple ordering plus the axiom that the ordering must contain in its domain a countable subset, dense with respect to the ordering in question.

A casual inspection of scientific theories suggests that the usual formulations are intrinsic rather than extrinsic in character, and therefore that the question of extrinsic formulations usually arises only in pure mathematics. This would also seem to be a happy result, for our philosophical intuition is surely that an intrinsic characterization is in general to be preferred to an extrinsic one.

However, the problem of intrinsic axiomatization of a scientific theory is more complicated and considerably more subtle than this remark would indicate. Fortunately, it is precisely by explicit consideration of the class of models of the theory that the problem can be put into proper perspective and formulated in a fashion that makes possible consideration of its exact solution. I shall give one simple example. The axioms for classical particle mechanics are ordinarily stated in such a way that a co-ordinate system, as a frame of reference, is tacitly assumed.

One effect of this is that relationships deducible from the axioms are not necessarily invariant with respect to Galilean transformations. We can view the tacit assumption of a frame of reference as an extrinsic aspect of the familiar characterizations of the theory. From the standpoint of the models of the theory, the difficulty in the standard axiomatizations of mechanics is that a large number of formally distinct models may be used to express the same mechanical facts. Each of these different models represents the tacit choice of a different frame of reference, but all models representing the same mechanical facts are related by Galilean transformations. It is thus fair to say that in this instance the difference between models related by Galilean transformations does not have any theoretical significance, and it may be regarded as a defect of the axioms that these trivially distinct models exist. It is important to realize that this point about models related by Galilean transformations is not the kind of point usually made under the heading of empirical interpretations of the theory.

It is a conceptual point that just as properly belongs to the theoretical side of physics. I have introduced this example here in order to provide a simple instance of how the explicit consideration of models can lead to a more subtle discussion of the nature of a scientific theory. It is certainly possible from a philosophical standpoint to maintain that particle mechanics as a scientific theory should be expressed only in terms of Galilean invariant relationships, and that the customary formulations are defective in this respect.

CO-ORDINATING DEFINITIONS
AND HIERARCHY OF THEORIES

I turn now to the second part of theories mentioned above. It is true that in the foregoing discussion we have been using the word "theory" to refer only to the first part of theories—that is, to the axiomatization of the theory or the expression of the theory as a logical calculus—but as I emphasized at the beginning, the necessity of providing empirical interpretation of a theory is just as important as the development of the formal side of the theory. My central point on this aspect of theories is that the story is much more complicated than the familiar remarks about co-ordinating definitions and empirical interpretations of theories would indicate. The kind of co-ordinating definitions often described by philosophers have their place in popular philosophical expositions of theories, but in the actual practice of testing scientific theories a more elaborate and more sophisticated formal machinery for relating a theory to data is required.

The concrete experience that scientists label an experiment cannot itself be connected to a theory in any complete sense. That experience must be put through a conceptual grinder that in many cases is excessively coarse. Once the experience is passed through the grinder, often in the form of the quite fragmentary records of the complete experiment, the experimental data emerge in canonical form and constitute a model of the experiment. It is this model of the experiment rather than a model of the theory for which direct co-ordinating definitions are provided. It is also characteristic that the model of the experiment is of a relatively different logical type from that of the model of the theory. It is common for the models of a theory to contain continuous functions or infinite sequences, but for the model of the experiment to be highly discrete and finitistic in character.

The assessment of the relation between the model of the experiment and some designated model of the theory is a characteristic fundamental problem of modern statistical methodology. What is important about this methodology for present purposes is that, in the first place, it is itself formal and theoretical in nature; secondly, it has been a typical function of this methodology to develop an elaborate theory of experimentation that intercedes between any fundamental scientific theory and raw experimental experience.

It is not possible in the confines of this essay to spell out the rather elaborate hierarchy of theories that are customarily interposed between the fundamental scientific theory and the experiments presumed to support it. My only point here is to make explicit the existence of this hierarchy and to point out that there is no simple procedure for giving co-ordinating definitions for a theory. It is even a bowdlerization of the facts to say that co-ordinating definitions are given to establish the proper connections between models of the theory and models of the experiment in the sense of the canonical form of the data just mentioned. The elaborate methods, for example, for estimating theoretical parameters in the model of the theory from models of the experiment are not adequately covered by a reference to co-ordinating definitions.

If someone asks, "What is a scientific theory?" it seems to me there is no simple response to be given. Are we to include as part of the theory the well-worked-out statistical methodology for testing the theory? If we are to take seriously the standard claims that the co-ordinating definitions are part of the theory, then it would seem inevitable that we must also include in a more detailed description of theories a methodology for designing experiments, estimating parameters and testing goodness-of-fit of the models of the theory. It does not seem to me important to give precise definitions of the form: X is a scientific theory if, and only if, so-and-so. What is important is to recognize that the existence of a hierarchy of theories arising from the methodology of experimentation for testing the fundamental theory is an essential ingredient of any sophisticated scientific discipline.

INSTRUMENTAL VIEW OF THEORIES

There is one view of scientific theories which is undoubtedly of considerable importance and which I have not yet mentioned. This is the view that theories are to be looked at from an instrumental viewpoint. The most important function of a theory, according to this view, is not to organize or assert statements that are true or false but to furnish material principles of inference that may be used in inferring one set of facts from another. Thus, in the familiar syllogism "all men are mortal; Socrates is a man; therefore, Socrates is mortal," the major premise "all men are mortal," according to this instrumental viewpoint, is converted into a principle of inference. And the syllogism now has only the minor premise "Socrates is a man."

From a logical standpoint it is clear that this is a fairly trivial move, and the question naturally arises if there is anything more substantial to be said about the instrumental viewpoint. Probably the most interesting argument for claiming that there is more than a verbal difference between these two ways of looking at theories or laws is the argument that when theories are regarded as principles of inference rather than as major premises, we are no longer concerned directly to establish their truth or falsity but to evaluate their *usefulness* in inferring new statements of fact. It is characteristic of discussions in this vein by philosophers that no genuinely original formal notions have arisen out of these discussions to displace the classical semantical notions of truth and validity. To talk, for instance, about laws having different jobs than statements of fact is trivial unless some systematic semantical notions are introduced to replace the standard analysis.

From another direction there has been one concerted serious effort to provide a formal framework for the evaluation of theories which replaces the classical concept of truth. What I have in mind is modern statistical decision theory. It is typical of statistical decision theory to talk about actions rather than statements. Once the focus is shifted from statements to actions, it seems quite natural to replace the concept of truth by that of expected loss or risk. It is appropriate to ask if a statement is true, but it does not make much sense to ask if it is risky. On the other hand, it is reasonable to ask how risky an action is, but not to ask if it is true. It is apparent that statistical decision theory, when taken literally, projects a more radical instrumental view of theories than does the view already sketched.

Theories are not regarded even as principles of inference but as methods of organizing evidence to decide which one of several actions to take. When theories are regarded as principles of inference, it is a straightforward matter to return to the classical view and to connect a theory as a principle of inference with the concept of a theory as a true major premise in an argument. The connection between the classical view and the view of theories as instruments leading to the taking of an action is certainly more remote and indirect.

Although many examples of applications of the ideas of statistical decision theory have been worked out in recent literature on the foundations of statistics, these examples in no case deal with complicated scientific theories, and I have seen no serious discussion of the treatment of scientific theories from the standpoint of statistical decision theory. Again, it is fair to say that when we want to talk about the evaluation of a sophisticated scientific theory, disciplines like statistical decision theory have not yet offered any genuine alternative to the semantical notions of truth and validity. In fact, even a casual inspection of the literature of statistical decision theory shows that in spite of the instrumental orientation of the fundamental ideas, formal development of the theory is wholly dependent on the standard semantical notions and in no sense replaces them.

What I mean by this is that in concentrating on the taking of an action as the terminal state of an inquiry the decision theorists have found it necessary to use standard semantical notions in describing evidence, their own theory, and so forth. For instance,

I cannot recall a single discussion by decision theorists in which particular observation statements are treated in terms of utility rather than in terms of their truth or falsity.

It seems apparent that statistical decision theory does not at the present time offer a genuinely coherent or deeply original new view of scientific theories. Perhaps future developments of decision theory will proceed in this direction. Be that as it may, there is one still more radical instrumental view that I would like to discuss as the final point to be covered in this essay. As I have already noted, it is characteristic of many instrumental analyses to distinguish the status of theories from the status of particular assertions of fact. It is the point of a more radical instrumental, behavioristic view of the use of language to challenge this distinction and to look at the entire use of language, including the statement of theories as well as of particular matters of fact, from a behavioristic viewpoint.

According to this view of the matter, all uses of language are to be analyzed with strong emphasis on the language users. It is claimed that the semantical analysis of modern logic gives a very inadequate account even of the cognitive uses of language, because it does not explicitly consider the production and reception of linguistic stimuli by speakers, writers, listeners, and readers. It is plain that for the behaviorist an ultimately meaningful answer to the question "What is a scientific theory?" cannot be given in terms of the kinds of concepts considered earlier. An adequate and complete answer can be given only in terms of an explicit and detailed consideration of both the producers and consumers of the theory. There is much that is attractive in this behaviorist way of looking at theories or language in general. What it lacks at present, however, is sufficient scientific depth and definiteness to serve as a genuine alternative to the precise notions of modern logic and semantics. Moreover, much of the language of models and theories discussed earlier in this chapter is surely so approximately correct that any behaviorist revision of our way of looking at theories must yield the ordinary talk about models and theories as a first approximation. It is a matter for the future to see whether or not the behaviorist's approach will deepen our understanding of the nature of scientific theories.

In current perspective, the methods and concepts of modern logic provide a satisfactory and powerful set of tools for analyzing the detailed structure of scientific theories. What would seem to be needed for the present is deeper and more detailed application of these tools to the job of analysis. I have tried to indicate what I think are some of the more fruitful directions for future investigation.

7 SCIENCE AND SIMPLICITY

Nelson Goodman

Should science be simple? Or must science be complex as the world is complex? Is simplicity a necessity, a luxury, or a vice? And is degree of simplicity determinable by objective measure or only by personal prejudice?

Phillip Frank has said that without simplicity there is no science. If we add that likewise without science there is no simplicity, we are on the way to understanding a good deal about science and simplicity and the relationship between them.

The search for simplicity in science is sometimes questioned on the ground that the world may actually be complex. This betrays a curious perversion of ideas. Rather than the simplicity of science being limited by the simplicity of the world, the simplicity of the world is limited by the simplicity of science. I do not mean that the world is complex until we simplify it. It is neither simple nor complex except relative to—as organized under—a given system. The world has as many different degrees of complexity as it has different structures, and it has as many different structures as there are different true ways of describing it. Without science, or some other mode of organization, there is no simplicity or complexity. To suppose that a simple system must be false if the world is complex is to suppose that a simple system must be false if an alternative complex system is true. The world, indeed, is as simple as any true system, but it is also as complex as any true system. And it is as grammatical, as ungrammatical, as coherent, as incoherent, as any true system. These descriptions apply to the world only obliquely, through applying to discourse about the world. We need not shun syntax or coherence or simplicity for fear the world is ungrammatical or incoherent or complex.

Still, does simplicity matter? The standard counsel seems to be to aim at truth and hope for simplicity. The objective of science, the reasoning runs, is to achieve a true system, and any effort to make a true system simpler is merely for the sake of making it prettier or more convenient. The injunction to seek truth regardless of simplicity has the self-righteous ring of a commandment not to put other gods before truth. Nevertheless, I submit that to seek a true system is to seek system as well as to seek truth. A mere collection of particular truths does not constitute science. Science is systematization, and systematization is simplification. If discovery of a way of dispensing with one of Peano's postulates or a way of defining one of three primitives of a system in terms of the other two does not seem momentous, that is only by comparison with the enormous systematization already effected through deriving vastly many theorems or terms from so meager a basis. Some economies are indeed minor, but complete disregard for economy would imply a willingness to take all terms and statements as primitive, to waive all definition and proof, and so to forgo all system. Without simplicity, there is no science.

But what is the measure of simplicity? Our confident judgments of comparative simplicity often conflict with one another; and we have ready at hand no very explicit or complete principles for resolving conflicts or filling gaps. Attempts at formulating a general criterion run so quickly into trouble that the problem is often dismissed as hopeless. Can we measure a property so multifarious, inconstant, and subjective? Before we give up, let's observe that the prospect of measuring physical size must once have looked equally dim for similar reasons. Size may mean total displacement or maximum diagonal or height and length and breadth, or any of many other quantities. It changes with time and circumstances, and our judgments of it vary with our physiology, prejudices, and point of view. Indeed, the case against the measurability of almost any property is overwhelming—until the property is measured. Consistency and objectivity are the products of measurement, not prerequisites for it.

To make a beginning, we may mark off a small but central part of the problem. Since systematization increases as the set of undefined ideas and unproved statements is reduced, what concerns us here is the simplicity of such a *basis* for a system. And since derivation of a system depends upon structural characteristics of the basis, what concerns us is formal or structural rather than psychological or semantic simplicity. For the moment, I shall put aside the question of the simplicity of sets of basic statements (that is, the question of axiomatic or postulational simplicity) to look first at the simplicity of sets of basic *terms*. Since the usual logical apparatus is common to all the systems under consideration, the question now before us is how to measure the structural simplicity of the basic *extralogical* vocabulary of a system.

One safe rule is that a basis is simpler than another if the first consists of some but not all the terms in the second. For example, if we succeed in deriving one of three primitive terms from the rest, we obviously effect a genuine saving. But so far we have no way of comparing the simplicity of two bases when each contains some term that the other does not. How can we broaden our rule to deal with such cases?

We might suppose that what counts is not merely whether one basis is included in another, but whether one is definable from the other; that a basis *A* is simpler than a basis *B* if *A* is definable from *B* but not *B* from *A*, and that two bases are equally simple if they are interdefinable. But this is plainly wrong. For since all the terms in any system are defined from the primitives, the set of all the terms would by this criterion be at least as simple as any narrower basis from which they can be defined. Thus we could never achieve any simpler basis for a system than by taking all of its terms as primitive and defining none of them. Obviously, then, the inverse of definitional yield is no measure of simplicity in any sense such that simplification of basis increases overall systematization. Yet many of the most sophisticated investigators of these problems have fallen victim to the error of taking definitional weakness for simplicity, of identifying power with complexity.

Let's try a different tack. Perhaps a basis properly included in another is simpler merely by virtue of containing fewer terms. Is the basis with more primitives always the more complex, then? Does simplicity always vary inversely with the number of terms in a basis? This popular and plausible notion quickly reduces to absurdity, for so long as all the terms in a basis have actual application, all can be combined into one. Consider, for example, the class-term or one-place predicate "conducts electricity," applying to certain materials, and the relation-term or two-place predicate "is denser than," relating certain materials to certain others. These can be compounded into the three-place predicate (with letters indicating the distinct blanks or predicate places) "x conducts electricity, and y is denser than z," and from this our original two predicates can be readily retrieved. But clearly no genuine simplification has been accomplished by this trick. If complexity were solely a matter of number of primitives, maximum simplicity could always be attained by thus trivially combining into one all the terms to be introduced into the system. The mere counting of primitives ignores differences in their internal complexity.

The next likely suggestion is to count the total number of predicate places in a basis; so that a basis consisting of two one-place predicates, for example, would have a complexity of 2, while a basis consisting of one three-place predicate would have a complexity of 3. This is indeed an improvement, but it still will not do. For while we have good reason for not considering a single predicate to be simpler than a set of several predicates having the same total number of places, we have no comparable reason for not considering the set to be simpler than the single predicate. We can always combine several applicable predicates into one without loss; we cannot always divide one applicable predicate into several without loss. For example, if we divide the two-place predicate "is a parent of" into the two one-place predicates "is a parent" and "has as a parent," we cannot retrieve the two-place predicate; for John may be a parent and William may have a parent without John's being a parent of William. The two-place predicate has some complexity that is missing in the set of two one-place predicates.

Perhaps we should stop grasping at surface hypotheses that

promptly let us down, and look rather for an underlying principle governing some of our firmest judgments of simplicity. Obviously, we do not simplify a basis by adding more primitives or by putting in a predicate with more places for a predicate with fewer places. And, as we have seen, no genuine simplification is achieved by combining several predicates into one. What have all these cases in common? The fact, I suggest, that in all of them the replacement of one basis by another can be accomplished by a purely routine procedure. An elementary canon of simplicity seems to be that a basis *A* is no simpler than a basis *B* if every basis of the same kind as *B* can always be replaced by some basis of the same kind as *A*. This may seem pretty timid and negative, and it surely needs a good deal of clarification, but it embodies the fundamental postulate for a calculus of structural simplicity.

One obscurity lies in what constitutes a *kind* of basis in the purview of this rule. If we take "kind" very narrowly, no two bases are of the same kind; and if we take it very broadly, every two bases are of the same kind. But the relevant classification here is according to certain structural properties. Determining just *which* properties calls for that mixture of arbitrary stipulation with faithfulness to common practice that is always needed in setting up standards of measurement, but I cannot now attempt to explain the particular reasons for the choice made. The relevant structural kinds of basis are those defined by giving the number of predicates and the number of places in each, together with any or no information concerning three further properties. I shall describe these properties briefly, but understanding of such technical details is not altogether essential for understanding the general procedure.

The first of the properties is *reflexivity*. Since every number is at least as great as itself, the two-place predicate "is at least as great as" relates every number to itself and is said to be reflexive. On the other hand, since no number is greater than itself, the two-place predicate "is greater than" is irreflexive. The second of the properties in question is *symmetry*. Since every number differs from every number that differs from it, the two-place predicate "differs from" applies in both directions if it applies in either, and this predicate is said to be symmetric. On the other hand, "is greater than" never applies in more than one direction between two numbers, and is thus asymmetric. The final property, a strengthened version of the familiar property of transitivity, might be called "loose-jointedness" or *self-completeness*. If 3 and 5 are both primes, and also 7 and 11 are both primes, then 3 and 11 are both primes. The two-place predicate "*x* and *y* are both primes" is *self-complete* in that if it relates one number to a second, and also relates a third to a fourth, it likewise relates the first to the fourth. Most ordinary two-place predicates, like "is greater than," are not self-complete; for example, although 3 is greater than 2, and 5 is greater than 4, still 3 is not greater than 4. Predicates with more than two places can be partially reflexive, partially symmetric, partially self-complete in a bewildering variety of ways.

The relevant structural kinds vary in comprehensiveness depending upon how specifically the requirements in terms of these properties are stated, and some kinds will include others. For example, the class of bases consisting of a single two-place predicate is a relevant kind; so also is the subclass of bases consisting of a single two-place symmetric predicate; and so on. Thus a basis may belong to several different relevant kinds. The narrowest relevant kind a basis belongs to may be called its *minimal kind*.

The principle of routine replaceability that stands as the first postulate of our calculus of structural simplicity can now be more clearly formulated. When replacement of one basis by a second requires nothing more than ordinary logic and the information that the first basis is of a given minimal kind, every basis of the same minimal kind as the first can be replaced by some basis of the same minimal kind as the second. The replacement is purely routine, and no simplification is achieved.

I cannot now follow through the development of the rest of the calculus, which requires four supporting postulates and provision for all applicable and inapplicable one-place and many-place predicates of elements and of classes, but let me cite some sample results. The complexity-value of a basis consisting of a single three-place predicate turns out to run from 1 to 15, depending upon what the minimal kind for the predicate is, as determined by the structural properties. The complexity-value of a basis consisting of a single four-place predicate ranges, similarly, from 1 to 59. Maximum complexity increases very rapidly with each increase in the total number of predicate places; but where the total number of predicate places is held constant, maximum complexity *decreases* as the number of predicates increases. Whereas a basis consisting of one three-place predicate has a maximum complexity of 15, a basis consisting of three one-place predicates has a complexity of 3. Reflexivity tends to *increase* complexity: compare a maximum complexity of 15 for a reflexive three-place predicate with a maximum complexity of 5 for an irreflexive one. On the other hand, both symmetry and self-completeness tend to *reduce* complexity: a three-place predicate that is either symmetric or self-complete has a maximum complexity of 3. And a predicate that is both symmetric and self-complete always has a complexity of exactly 1, no matter how many places it may have. All this may suggest how much more than a mere count of predicates or predicate places must be considered in measuring the complexity of a basis.

When we turn to the set of unproved extralogical *statements* of a system, the problem of their simplicity looks much like the problem of the simplicity of the set of undefined extralogical terms. In the first place, we must clearly distinguish complexity from strength here, too; for since all the theorems of a system are derivable from the postulates, the set of all the statements of the system is no stronger than the set of postulates. Thus, if weakness were the measure of simplicity, we would achieve as simple a basis by merely postulating all the statements of the system as by deriving most of them from the others. In the second place, mere number of postulates is no measure of complexity, for all the postulates of any system can be reduced to one merely by conjoining them.

These comparisons may lead us to suspect that the clue to measuring simplicity of postulates, as of primitive terms, lies in a principle of replaceability. But this reasonable hope is frustrated by a paradoxical discovery. Virtually any set of extralogical postulates can be completely eliminated, by a purely

74

routine procedure, without loss of deductive yield or increase in the complexity of the set of basic terms. As an illustration, suppose we have a system with the single primitive two-place predicate "intersects" and the single postulate of symmetry—that is, that everything intersects whatever intersects it. Now proceed as follows: instead of "intersects," take as primitive another word, say "cuts," for the same relation. Then introduce "intersects" into the system by the following definition: x intersects y if either x cuts y or y cuts x. From this definition, without any postulate, we can easily prove that "intersects" is symmetric. A general method has been found for so replacing postulates by definitions.

Should we, then, consider definitions to be postulates in determining the complexity of a postulate set? There are two troubles with this. First, definitions function in a system as devices for abbreviating theorems and can themselves be dropped without essential sacrifice of deductive yield. Second, we have seen earlier that our set of definitions inevitably becomes more intricate and comprehensive as we reduce the complexity of our set of undefined terms; hence we are working at cross purposes if we take the complexity of a set of definitions to be an indication of any complexity in the basis for a system.

As yet we have no satisfying answer to this puzzle, and no feasible way of measuring complexity of sets of postulates. But we are at much too early a stage in our investigation to despair of finding a better approach.

So far, I have been speaking of structural simplicity alone. I have said nothing of semantic or psychological simplicity. And I have treated simplicity as tantamount to systematization, and as complementary to, rather than as either contributing to or competing with, truth in science. But now I shall go much further. Simplicity, in at least some respect, is a test of truth.

If this seems simple-minded scientific treason, consider how we proceed in science. Suppose we are studying the relationship between the volume and pressure of a gas at constant temperature. We make many observations and plot them on a graph. We find that all the plotted points fall along a certain neat curve, and the function describing that curve is then incorporated in our theory and used for predicting further cases.

75

Notice, however, that no matter how many points we have plotted, infinitely many curves of different degrees of jaggedness or complexity pass through all these points. Any prediction whatever concerning an unobserved case could be made by using one or another of these curves. Our chosen curve has no more direct evidence in its favor than does any of the others. Simplicity of some sort governs the choice, and, without such a criterion, even the most comprehensive collection of data would stand neutral with respect to untested cases.

Take another example. Suppose a botanist finds that all the elm trees he examines, in many localities and under varying conditions, are deciduous. He may very well adopt the hypothesis that all elm trees are deciduous. He is unlikely to choose, instead, any of the countless other hypotheses that can claim exactly the same evidence. Among these, for example, if no trees in Smithtown happen to have been examined, are the following:

1. All elm trees everywhere, and also all pines in Smithtown, are deciduous.

2. All elm trees, except perhaps for those in Smithtown, are deciduous.

3. All other elm trees, but not those in Smithtown, are deciduous.

Moreover, any statement that combines the assertion that all the examined elm trees are deciduous with the ascription of any property whatsoever to unexamined things will belong on this list. The chosen hypothesis, "all elm trees are deciduous," is not the weakest; indeed, the conservative policy of choosing only the weakest hypothesis would prohibit going beyond the evidence at all. Nor is the chosen hypothesis the strongest; indeed, for any hypothesis that does venture beyond the evidence there is an alternative hypothesis that gives conflicting results for the unexamined cases. We take neither the safest nor the boldest course but the one that is in some sense or other the simplest.

Here and in the choice among curves, simplicity is used as a test of truth. That does not mean that we choose the simplest hypothesis even if it is controverted by the evidence, but rather that among hypotheses fitting the known cases we tend to choose the simplest hypothesis for judging the unknown cases. The simplicity involved here is surely not the structural simplicity I was talking about a few minutes ago, or a purely formal property at all. It has something to do not only with brevity or grammatical simplicity of statement but also with the familiarity of the language employed. The pragmatic factor of linguistic habit clearly plays a fundamental role in simplicity of this kind.

But what justification have we for so using simplicity as a test of truth? Can there be any ground for supposing that a statement has a better chance of being true merely because it is shorter and grammatically simpler and in familiar words or symbols? We are here in the middle of the notorious problem of justifying induction and we must be on guard; for that problem in some formulations turns out to be empty, and in others to be very different from what it seems on the surface. All I can say here is that some such test as simplicity is indispensable if we are to make predictions at all, and that it is justifiable in the sense and to the degree that science in general is justifiable.

If your scientific sensibilities have been shocked by the idea that simplicity is a test of truth, they are now in for an even heavier blow. For in science the consideration of simplicity must often override that of truth. We must not ignore the facts, but truth and simplicity often contend with one another, and truth cannot always win. Consider again, for example, the matter of fitting a curve to plots on a graph. Seldom does the chosen curve pass exactly through each of the points plotted; sometimes it may miss them all. Rather than choosing the simplest among the complex curves that just fit the evidence, we choose among simple curves the one that comes nearest to fitting the evidence. Most of our scientific theories are neat approximations, less controlled than inspired by the evidence. Failing to transcend the detailed results of observation and experiment is as bad as playing fast and loose with them. Theory and fact have to be adjusted to each other. The able scientist develops a keen sense of when to yield to recalcitrant observations by modifying his theory and when to blame them on dirty test tubes and faulty instruments.

In review, then, I have argued that there is no science without simplicity—and no simplicity without something like science. I have discussed some measures of simplicity, and simplicity as a measure of systematization. And I have argued that simplicity not only functions as a test of truth but sometimes outweighs truth. What is important about simplicity, though, is not arguments for its importance, but painstaking analysis of it into component factors, study of how they function in relation to each other and to other factors, and development of means of measurement. Much of this work remains to be done, and in this essay I could not give any adequate idea of even the beginnings that have been made. I have tried only to attract your interest to a new and vital aspect of the science of science.

8 SCIENTIFIC EXPLANATION

Carl G. Hempel

Among the many factors that have stimulated and sustained scientific inquiry throughout its long history, there are two enduring concerns that have provided the most important motives for man's scientific efforts.

The first is of a practical nature: man constantly seeks to improve his strategic position vis-à-vis the world he lives in, and to this end he tries to find effective ways of predicting the course of the events in his environment and, whenever possible, controlling them to his advantage. How successful scientific research has been in the pursuit of this end is shown by the vast and steadily widening range of its technological applications, both constructive and destructive, which have put their characteristic imprint on every aspect of contemporary civilization.

The second basic motive for man's scientific quest involves no such practical concerns: it lies simply in his intellectual curiosity, in his deep and persistent desire to know and understand the world he lives in. So strong is this urge for knowledge and understanding that in the absence of adequate factual information, myths will often be invoked to answer questions about the What and the Why of empirical phenomena. Gradually, however, such myths give way to concepts and theories arrived at by scientific research in the natural sciences as well as in psychology and in the sociological and historical disciplines.

What is the nature of the explanations that empirical science in this broad sense can offer us, and what sort of understanding of the world do they convey?

DEDUCTIVE EXPLANATION BY COVERING LAWS

An explanation in the sense that concerns us here is basically an answer to the question why a given event occurred or why a certain state of affairs obtains. Questions of this kind are often answered in causal terms. Thus, it might be explained that the lengthening of a copper rod was caused by an increase in its temperature; or that a sudden deflection of a compass needle was caused by an electric current that was switched on in a nearby circuit; or that the moon persists in its orbital motion about the earth because of the gravitational attraction that the earth and the moon exert upon each other.

But as Hume has taught us, the assertion that an event of a certain kind C causes an event of a certain other kind E implies the claim that any occurrence of C is regularly accompanied by an occurrence of E; for example, that in any case when the temperature of a copper rod is raised, its length increases. Thus, causal explanations presuppose general laws of nature that connect the specified cause with the effect to be explained. For the explanations just mentioned, science can supply the relevant laws; these govern the thermal expansion of metals, the magnetic effects of electric currents, and the relative motion of two bodies under the influence of their mutual gravitational attraction.

If the relevant laws are explicitly stated, the resulting explanation can be put into the form of a deductive argument in which the occurrence of the event in question is inferred from a set of premises which specify (1) the relevant laws and (2) those particular antecedent circumstances which in everyday parlance are said to have caused the event. For example, our explanation of the lengthening of a copper rod would take the form of an argument with two premises: (1) the general law that any copper rod grows longer when its temperature is raised, and (2) the statement that the given rod was made of copper and that its temperature had been raised. These premises deductively imply the conclusion that the rod increased in length, which is the event to be explained. Thus, the explanatory statement that the lengthening of the rod was caused by the increase in its temperature is replaced by an argument which no longer contains the word "cause" or its cognates. Briefly, it is to the effect that the given copper rod was heated, and all heated copper rods grow longer; and that, therefore, the given rod increased in length.

Generally, it may be said that the technical vocabulary in which scientific hypotheses and theories are expressed does not contain such words as "cause" and "causal factor," and that an account in terms of causes is acceptable as an explicit explanation in science only as far as the causal attribution it makes can be substantiated and replaced by statements of corresponding laws. Such laws will normally take a precise quantitative form. This is the case, for example, with the laws for the thermal expansion of metals, which accordingly make it possible to explain not only the fact but also the extent of the change in length that occurs in response to temperature changes.

In informal, non-technical everyday language an explanation will often be expressed elliptically by means of a simple "because"-statement which mentions only one or a very few of the many items that would have to be specified if the explanation were to be formulated as an explanatory scientific argument. Take, for example, the statement that the moon keeps moving about the earth because of the mutual gravitational attraction of the two bodies. In an explicit restatement of this sketchy account the explanatory premises might include Newton's laws of gravitation and of motion as well as particular statements about the masses of the two bodies and their relative positions and velocities at some particular time. And the deduction of the desired conclusion from these premises requires, not simple syllogistic reasoning, but the powerful mathematical techniques of the calculus.

Explanations of the kind we have just examined may be called *explanations by deductive subsumption under covering laws,* or briefly, deductive explanations. A deductive explanation of a given event shows that the event resulted from specified particular circumstances in accordance with certain general laws; thus it enables us to understand the event by making us aware that, in view of those laws and particular circumstances, its occurrence was to be expected.

81

So far we have considered deductive explanations which in non-technical language would be formulated as causal statements. But the explanatory power of deductive subsumption under general laws extends far beyond cases of this kind. Suppose, for example, we find that a given simple pendulum takes two seconds to complete a full swing. This might be explained by noting that the pendulum has a length of 100 cm, and by invoking the law that the period of swing of any simple pendulum of length L equals $2\Pi\sqrt{L/g}$, where g is the constant acceleration of free fall; this law yields a value close to two seconds for the period of our pendulum. While this explanation is deductive, it does not correspond to a causal account; we would not say that the pendulum's requiring two seconds for a full swing is *caused* by the fact that it has a length of 100 cm.

All our examples so far deal with the explanation of particular events. But science seeks to answer the question "Why?" not only for this or that individual occurrence but also for the uniformities and regularities expressed by general laws. Thus, in the case of the pendulum, we might proceed to ask: Why does any simple pendulum conform to the law that its period equals $2\Pi\sqrt{L/g}$? Similarly, we might ask why in any free fall the velocity is proportional to the falling time, as asserted by Galileo's law; or why all planetary motions exhibit the striking regularities expressed by Kepler's laws.

To many of these questions science offers answers which, interestingly, have again the character of a deductive explanation. A uniformity expressed by an empirical law is then explained by showing that it holds in virtue of, or more precisely, as a consequence of, certain other, more general, laws or of more fundamental and comprehensive theoretical principles. For example, the law for the simple pendulum as well as Galileo's and Kepler's laws can all be shown to be special consequences of the basic laws of mechanics and of gravitation; similarly, the optical laws of reflection and refraction and of shadow formation can all be derived from the basic principles of the electromagnetic-wave theory of light.

To develop theories which will thus explain the regularities expressed by empirical laws is one of the foremost objectives of scientific endeavor, and many a scientist will hold that only when we can offer explanatory theories have we attained genuine scientific understanding. At any rate, a sound theoretical explanation will usually broaden as well as deepen our understanding of a given field of inquiry. Newton's theory of motion and of gravitation, for example, *broadened* the scope of scientific understanding by accounting for a vastly wider range of phenomena than do the previously established laws which the theory explains. And the theory *deepened* our understanding not only in the sense of reducing all those other laws to one common system of underlying basic principles but also by showing that the previously accepted empirical laws, such as Kepler's and Galileo's, do not hold strictly, but only in approximation.

For example, Newton's principles imply that since every planet is subject to gravitational pull not only from the sun, but also from the other planets, the planets will not move in strict accordance with Kepler's laws, but will show certain perturbations; and Newton's theory implies equally that the acceleration of free fall near the earth is not strictly a constant, as asserted by Galileo's law, but changes with the distance of the falling body from the earth's center of gravity.

PROBABILISTIC EXPLANATION BY COVERING LAWS

All the explanatory laws and theoretical principles I have mentioned so far have one important logical characteristic in common. They are of *strictly universal form*: that is, they assert the existence of certain unexceptional uniform connections; for example, between the volume, the pressure, and the temperature of a gas; or between the temperature and the length of a copper rod. Laws of strictly universal form differ fundamentally from those of another type which, during the past hundred years or so, have steadily gained in scientific importance, namely, laws of *probabilistic form*.

In a nutshell, the difference between the two is this: A law of universal form asserts that in all cases without exception when conditions of a specified kind C are realized, a phenomenon of a certain kind E occurs; whereas a probabilistic law states that under conditions C there is a statistical probability r for the occurrence of E, so that, in the long run, the proportion of cases of C that result in E will be r. The laws stating the half-lives of radioactive substances are of this kind; for example, to say that the half-life of polonium is three minutes is to say that the probability for a polonium atom to undergo radioactive decay within any given three-minute interval is one half. This law can be used to explain why, of a given initial amount of polonium, only half is left after three minutes, only one fourth after six minutes, and so on. The basic principles of quantum theory provide another example of probabilistic laws; and so do certain laws of genetics, such as those which serve to explain the proportions of plants with white, red and pink flowers that are found among the hybrids obtained by crossing a pure-white-flowered and a pure-red-flowered strain.

Explanations based on such probabilistic laws I will call *probabilistic explanations*. Because of the statistical character of the laws it invokes, a probabilistic explanation shows only that, in view of the specified laws and particular circumstances, the phenomenon to be explained was to be expected with more or less high *probability;* whereas a deductive explanation shows that, given the truth of the explanatory information, the occurrence of the phenomenon in question follows with deductive certainty.

But deductive and probabilistic explanations agree in their essential reliance on covering laws; both explain a given phenomenon by showing that it occurs in conformance with such laws. I think that this is indeed a common characteristic of all scientific explanations, and more specifically that all scientific explanations of empirical phenomena are basically covering-law explanations of the deductive or of the probabilistic variety. I will try to amplify and support this idea as I proceed.

EXPLANATION AS REDUCTION TO THE FAMILIAR

It is sometimes said that an explanation should make us understand an unfamiliar or novel fact by reducing or assimilating it to facts with which we are already familiar. But this idea surely does not adequately characterize scientific explanation.

Quite apart from the vagueness and subjectivity of the notion of familiarity here invoked, this conception suggests, first of all, that familiar facts require no explanation. But while in our everyday affairs we might agree with this view, science clearly does not. Indeed, science has gone to great lengths in an effort to explain such "familiar" phenomena as the changing tides, thunderstorms, and rainbows, the blue color of the sky, the similarities between parents and their offspring, our slips of pen, tongue and memory, and many others. The point is strikingly illustrated by Olbers' paradox. In 1826 the German astronomer Heinrich Olbers noted that as a consequence of a few simple and extremely plausible assumptions, including some standard laws of optics and the hypothesis that the stars are distributed uniformly throughout the universe, the sky should appear very bright in all directions, day and night. Thus, the fact that it is dark at night, which surely is as familiar as any, was seen as posing a serious problem that called for an explanation. A solution has recently been suggested on the basis of the cosmological theory of the expanding universe; for it can be shown that the uniform recession of distant sources of light would account for the fact that it is dark at night. Here, then, a very familiar fact is explained in terms of a theory that incorporates some unfamiliar and indeed quite extraordinary ideas.

This example also illustrates a second point—namely, that rather than reduce the unfamiliar to the familiar, science will often do just the opposite: it will explain familiar facts by powerful theoretical principles which may strike us as quite unfamiliar and unintuitive, but which account for a wide variety of phenomena and are well supported by the results of careful tests.

The view that to explain is to reduce the unfamiliar to the familiar can be deceptive in yet another way. Consider, for example, an explanation of a thunderstorm in terms of the wrath of an angered deity, or consider a vitalistic account of some self-regulatory biological process as being effected by an entelechy or vital force. These explanatory attempts may well convey a sense of at-homeness, of familiarity, with the striking phenomena in question: but they afford no genuine understanding of them. Vitalistic accounts, for example, do not tell us in a general fashion under what conditions a vital force will manifest itself, what specific form its manifestation will take, and to what extent it will compensate for disturbing influences that have been exerted upon an organism. Such accounts, then, do not indicate what occurrences are to be expected in this or that kind of situation; consequently they cannot form the basis of any scientific explanation.

By contrast, the explanation of planetary motion in terms of the Newtonian theory does tell us what gravitational forces will be exerted upon a given planet by the sun and by other planets, given their masses and their distances; and it tells us further what kind of motion is to be expected as a result of the action of those forces. Thus, while both accounts invoke certain factors that cannot be directly observed—one of them, vital forces, the other gravitational ones—the latter has explanatory power while the former does not. This is due precisely to the fact that gravitational forces are held to conform to specifically stated laws, whereas vitalistic doctrines offer no laws governing vital forces.

Thus, it is laws that are essential for an explanation, but not the familiarity of the images and associations that the words "gravitational force" and "vital force" may conjure up in our minds. The laws invoked in explaining a phenomenon also have predictive import. They will predict, first of all, similar occurrences under similar circumstances—for example, Keplerian motion for the planets of other stars. And the laws may also predict "new" phenomena quite different from those they were invoked to explain: the Newtonian laws not only explain Kepler's laws of planetary motion and Galileo's law of free fall but also predict, given the flattened shape of the earth, that the acceleration of free fall is greater at the poles than at the equator. Indeed, such predictions provide a means of testing the soundness of a given explanation; and an explanation whose covering laws or theoretical principles fail on this score has to be abandoned. Such was the fate, for example, of the explanation of combustion offered by the phlogiston theory.

No such fate can befall explanations in terms of myths or metaphors or vital forces: since they do not tell us what to expect under any empirical conditions, no empirical finding can ever discredit them. But such absolute immunity from disconfirmation is not an asset but a fatal defect when judged by the goals of science. For science seeks to establish an objectively testable and empirically well-supported body of factual knowledge. An account in terms of myths or metaphors, however appealing it may be intuitively, has no implications concerning empirical facts and thus has no logical bearing on them at all; it is a *pseudo explanation,* an explanation in appearance only.

EXPLANATION BY REASONS

I suggested earlier that the explanation of any empirical phenomenon involves its deductive or probabilistic subsumption under covering laws or theories. Now, it is widely held that while this might typically be the case in the natural sciences, it surely is not so in other fields of research, particularly in the psychological, sociological, and historical study of human thought and action. According to this view, an adequate explanation of an action requires, not a specification of causes or covering laws, but of motivating reasons; these will include, first, the objectives the agent intended to achieve, and second, his beliefs about relevant empirical matters, such as what alternative courses of action were open to him, and what their probable consequences would be.

On one recent version of this view, which has its roots in Collingwood's work, an explanation of a given action must show that the action "makes sense" in the light of the agent's reasons; or, more precisely, that it was the appropriate or reasonable thing to do under the given circumstances, which include especially the agent's objectives and beliefs. But—leaving aside the problem of standards of appropriateness—the explanatory information that a given action X was the appropriate thing to do under the given circumstances does not, as an explanation should, entitle us to conclude: hence, it was to be expected that the agent would do

X. To justify that conclusion, we clearly need a further explanatory assumption, roughly to the effect that the agent is the kind of person who will generally perform whatever action is appropriate in the situation in which he finds himself. But an explanatory assumption of this kind makes a general claim and thus plays the role of a covering law, though the law is of a somewhat peculiar kind: it concerns the way a *particular* agent will generally act in a variety of circumstances. The Oxford philosopher Gilbert Ryle, who has dealt in some detail with the explanatory use of such generalizations, calls them law-like sentences.

Thus it is true that psychologists and historians as well as people in their everyday dealings with each other will often invoke motivating reasons in order to explain human actions; but this does not show that the explanations thus arrived at do not presuppose covering laws or at least law-like statements. Let me rephrase the reason briefly in more general terms: Whenever, in an effort to explain a person's actions, we attribute to him certain beliefs, intentions, moral standards, character traits, or the like, we assert by implication certain law-like generalizations, of universal or of probalistic form, about the way the agent will behave under various circumstances; and it is on these generalizations that our explanation rests. Hence, even the explanation of human behavior by reference to psychological characteristics and to motivating reasons is basically explanation by subsumption under covering laws.

This conclusion, and the arguments that led us to it, clearly do not imply a narrowly mechanistic view of man and his actions. What our considerations suggest is rather this: explanations in all areas of scientific inquiry share certain basic characteristics; and deductive and probabilistic subsumption under covering laws constitute modes of explanation that reach far beyond causal and mechanical explanation. In particular, subsumption under covering generalizations is implicit also in those explanatory accounts that seek to exhibit the influence of conscious and unconscious motives and of ideas and ideals on the shaping of human decisions and actions and thus on the course of man's history.

9 OBSERVATION AND INTERPRETATION

Norwood Russell Hanson

1. Philosophers often conjoin the terms "observation" and "interpretation." They go together like "peaches and cream," "ham and eggs," or "fish and chips." But familiar conjunctions like these latter differ from observation-and-interpretation. We can speak of peaches *before* the cream has been poured. Ham can be had without eggs. Fish are distinct from chips.

However, what is an observation *before* it is interpreted? What could interpretation-independent observations be like? Are the two separable at all?

2. I contend that observation and interpretation are inseparable, not just in that they never *do* occur independently, but rather in that it is inconceivable that either could obtain in total isolation from the other. A model more suitable than peaches and cream, or ham and eggs, would be pairs like "warp and woof," "lift and drag"—indeed, "matter and form."

There *might* be arguments for conceptually separating the warp from the woof in a fabric, the lift from the drag on an airfoil, and the matter from the form of a statue. Nonetheless, in such cases *argument* is required. I place "observation and interpretation" in this category of conceptual pairs. Just as actually separating the warp from the woof destroys the fabric, and physically separating the lift from the drag on a wing will render an aircraft uncontrollable—and just as "separating matter from form in a statue" describes nothing intelligible at all—so also, slicing the incoming signals of sensation from an appreciating of the significance of those signals would destroy what we know as *scientific observation*. The Neopositivistic model of observation,

89

wherein our sensational data registration, and our intellectual constructions thereupon, are cleft atwain, is an analytical stroke tantamount to logical butchery. This results only in the expiry of the heart of natural science, at the pulse of which is the struggle toward more intelligently encountered, reasonably comprehended, and theoretically appreciated *observations*.

3. Many philosophers will, even here, have lost sympathy with me. Their analyses concern "the data" of scientific observation—its "cash value." Where do people err in reporting their observations? Usually, just in exaggerating their descriptions of what they encountered, not in their having received the wrong sense signals from the outer world. People *will* speak of seeing water—when actually wood decomposes if floated in what they see (in fact, it's a weak acid). Or they'll speak of seeing ice—although it won't float on ordinary water (it's frozen deuterium, in fact). They'll speak of looking through ordinary glass—not realizing that when turned 90° it becomes opaque (being in fact polaroid).

So these descriptions of observations were in error, not because the observers' sense organs failed to pick up signals impinging on them, but because the observers jumped beyond the *pure* observations to speculations by far surpassing what the basic data warranted. If only observers would restrict themselves to the color patches they see, the buzzes and tinkles they hear, the rough and smooth surfaces they touch, and the sweet or sour taste of things —only then could the strictly empirical basis of an observation be detached from the theoretical embroidery attached thereto; only then can the properties of nature be demarcated from the properties specified in the observers' theories about nature.

Of course, such a positivistic recommendation is compatible with the recognition that, within contemporary science, what are *called* "observations" are really intricate mixtures of empirical components and theoretical frosting; apparently what is called "scientific observation" is genuine observation to but a small degree—so runs the recommendation. Unless we remain alert to this, our philosophies of science may issue in the apparently absurd suggestion that two reliable observers *could* encounter the same physical phenomenon and yet register different observations. But if two well-made cameras were aimed at the same phenomenon, they would take the same picture. And two tape recorders would record the same noises if similarly placed with respect to an acoustical source. Similarly, continues the recommendation, two "ideal" scientific observers should make the same observations; what they then proceed to make *of* those observations is another matter—concerning which philosophers have also said much. But two observers, especially when their theoretical commitments differ, can make the same observations only insofar as their encounters with phenomena are described strictly in phenomenalistic, or "sense-datum," terms. Differences between them are manifested only *after* taking in the data.

FIRST OBSERVE, THEN THEORIZE

4. In the interests of a more realistic philosophy of science, however, I will press for the opposite conclusion. I will even argue for what seems so absurd to the phenomenalist, that two observers, equally well equipped, may confront the same phenomenon, and yet make quite different observations. This, not because they are busily clamping different theories onto the otherwise "pure" data—but rather because they are *observing: to observe X is to observe X as something or other.*

Observing is an experience. A retinal reaction or an olfactory or tactile reaction is only a physical state—a photochemical or pressure-sensitive excitation. Physiologists have not always distinguished experiences and physical states. People see, not their eyes. Cameras and eyeballs are blind. Attempts to locate within the organs of sight (or within the neurological reticulum behind the eyes), some nameable called "seeing" or "observing" may be summarily dismissed. There is more to seeing than meets the eyeball. And there is much more to scientific observation than merely standing alert with sense organs "at the ready."

Consider the Necker cube, so familiar to psychologists. The twelve connected lines seem configured in the standard "box-like" way. Do we all see the same thing? Some will see an ice cube viewed from below. Others will see it from above. Still others will view the figure as a polygonally-cut gem. Some see only crisscrossed lines in a plane. Others will see it as an aquarium, a wire frame for a kite, or any of a number of other things. Do we, then, all see the same thing? If we do, how can these differences be explained?

Here the phenomenalist's "formula" re-enters: "These are different *interpretations* of what all normal observers see in common." Retinal reactions to a Necker cube are virtually identical; so too with our visual sense data, since our drawings (for example, on grid paper) of what we see will have the same content—they could even be congruent. The drawn Necker cube is simply observed now as a box from below, now as a cube from above; one does not first soak up an optical pattern and then clamp an interpretation onto it.

"But," comes the phenomenalistic retort, "seeing a Necker cube first as a box from below and then as a cube from above *involves* interpreting the lines differently in each case." Then for two observers to have a different interpretation of a Necker cube *is* for them to observe something different. This need not mean that they see exactly the same thing and then interpret it differently.

Besides, the word "interpretation" is occasionally useful as we now employ it. We know where it applies and where it does not. Thucydides presented the facts objectively; Herodotus put an interpretation on them. The word does not apply to everything; it has a meaning. Can interpreting *always* be going on when we observe things? Sometimes, perhaps, as when the hazy outline of a combine harvester looms up before us on a foggy morning and, with effort, we finally identify it. Is this the "interpretation" which is active when bicycles and boxes are clearly observed? Is it active when the Necker cube snaps into its "other" perspective? There was a time when Herodotus was half-through with his interpretation of the Greco-Persian Wars. Could there be a time when one is half-through interpreting a Necker cube as a box from above—or as anything else?

"But the interpretation takes very little time—it is instantaneous." Instantaneous interpretation hails from the same limbo that produced unsensed sensibilia, unconscious inference, incorrigible statements, and negative facts. These are notions philosophers force on the world in order to preserve some pet epistemological or metaphysical theory.

Only in contrast to "eureka" situations (like perspective reversals, where one has not even time to interpret the data) is it clear what is meant by saying that although Thucydides could have put an interpretation on history, he did not. Whether or not a historian is advancing an interpretation is an empirical question: we know what would count as evidence one way or the other. But whether we are employing an interpretation when we see a Necker cube in a certain way seems not to be empirical.

What *could* count as evidence? In no ordinary sense of "interpret" do I interpret the Necker cube differently when its perspective reverses for me. And if there is some extraordinary sense of the word, it is not clear, in ordinary language, or in philosophical language, or in scientific language what this might be. To insist that different reactions to a Necker cube *must* lie in the interpretations put on some common visual experience is just to reiterate (without reasons) that an observing of X must be no more than the same sensation registration for all observers looking at X.

But, it will be countered, "I see the figure as a box" means: "I am having the visual experience I always have when I interpret the figure as a box, or when I look at a box . . ." Now really, if I meant this, I ought to know it directly. I ought to be able to refer to that experience directly and not only by indirect references to boxes. This is just what is meant by calling sense data "logical destructions out of material objects."

Everyday accounts of the experiences appropriate to viewing a Necker cube do not require visual grist going into an intellectual mill; theories and interpretations are "there" in the observing, from the outset.

Consider further all those reversible perspective figures which appear in textbooks on Gestalt psychology: the tea tray, the shifting staircase, the tunnel. Each of these can be seen as concave, convex, or as flat. Do I observe something different each time, or do I only interpret what I see in a different way? To interpret is to think, to do something *à la* Herodotus; observing is the having of an experience. The different ways in which these

Gestalt figures are seen are not due to different thoughts lying behind the visual reactions. What could "spontaneous" mean if such reactions as these are not spontaneous? One does not think of anything special; one may not think at all. Nor does one interpret. One just observes, now a staircase as from above, now a staircase as from below.

There is a range of other variable figures—those called "variable *aspect* figures." The most famous is W. Köhler's "Goblet-and-Faces": one can see a Venetian glass centered against a dark background, or two profiles facing each other. Again we "take" the same retinal/cortical/sense-datum picture of the configuration; our drawings on grid paper might be indistinguishable. Yet I see an ornate goblet and you see two men staring at one another. Do we see the same thing? Yes—in some elementary sense. Do we observe the same thing? Perhaps not. I draw my goblet. You say, "That's just what I saw, two men in a staring contest." What must be done to get you to see what I see? When attention shifts from the cup to the faces, does one's visual picture change? How? What is it that changes? What could change? Nothing optical or sensational is modified. Yet one observes different things. The organization of what one observes has changed.

5. Imagine now a glass-and-metal instrument replete with wires, reflectors, screws, clamps, and pushbuttons. Imagine this instrument placed before a trained physicist, one who at that moment is holding his two-month-old infant on his knee. Do the physicist and the infant observe the same thing when looking at such an X-ray tube? Yes, and no. Yes: they are visually aware of the same object. No: the *ways* in which they are aware are profoundly different. Seeing is not only the having of a visual experience; it is also the way in which the experience is had. This does not mean that the physicist is busy with intra-cranial activities absent in the infant's case; this may or may not be so. Both simply see what is before them. The physicist sees a glass-and-metal instrument. The infant takes in precisely the same optical data, but may be observing nothing in particular.

In college the physicist had gazed at this instrument each day. Returning now, after years in industry and research, his eye lights upon the same object. Does he see the same thing as he did then? Now he observes the instrument in terms of electrical circuit theory, thermodynamic theory, the theories of metal and glass structure, thermionic emission, optical transmission, refraction, diffraction, atomic theory, quantum theory, special relativity, and the problems of atomic energy and nuclear machines.

"Granted, one learns these things, but they all figure in the *interpretation* the physicist puts on what he sees. Though the layman sees exactly what the physicist sees, he cannot interpret it in the same way because he has not learned so much."

Is the physicist doing any more than just seeing? No; he *does* nothing over and above what the layman does, what he himself did as a young student, or what his child does when he sees an X-ray tube. What are you doing at this moment over and above reading these words? Are you interpreting marks on paper? Would this ever be a natural way of speaking? Perhaps—if English were not your native language; which makes the same point in reverse. Would an infant see what you are now seeing when you see words and sentences and he sees nothing but marks and spaces? One does nothing beyond looking and seeing when he dodges automobiles, glances at a friend, or notices a cat in the garden.

"The physicist and the layman see the same thing" it may be objected, "but they do not make the same thing of it." The layman can make nothing of it. The child can make nothing of it. Nor is that just a figure of speech. I can make nothing of the Arab word for "ice cube," though my purely auditory impressions may be indistinguishable from those of the Arab who hears his word for "ice cube" quite clearly. I must learn Arabic before I can hear what he hears. The layman must learn some physics before he can observe what the physicist observes. As the great astronomer William Herschel observed: "Seeing is . . . an art which must be learn't."

FIRST LEARN, THEN OBSERVE

The creature that has learned nothing can observe nothing—that's part of the semantical content of the word "observe."

As Pierre Duhem once wrote:

Enter a laboratory; approach the table crowded with an assortment of apparatus, an electric cell, silk-covered copper wire, small cups of mercury, spools, a mirror mounted on an iron bar; the experimenter is inserting into small openings the metal ends of ebony-headed pins; the iron oscillates and the mirror attached to it throws a luminous band upon a celluloid scale; the forward-backward motion of this spot enables the physicist to observe the minute oscillations of the iron bar. *But ask him what he is doing.* Will he answer, "I am studying the oscillations of an iron bar which carries a mirror?" No, he will say that he is measuring the electrical resistance of the spools. If you are astonished, if you ask him what his words mean, what relation they have with the phenomenon he has been observing and which you have noted at the same time as he, he will answer that your question requires a long explanation and that you should take a course in electricity.

The visitor must learn physics before he can observe what the physicist observes. Only then will the context throw into relief those features in the phenomena which the physicist observes as indicating resistance. This obtains in all cases of observation. It is all interest-directed and context-dependent. Attention is rarely directed to the space *between* the leaves of a tree. Still, consider what was involved in Robinson Crusoe's seeing a vacant space in the sand as a footprint. Our attention naturally rests on objects and events which, because of our selective interests, dominate the visual field. What a blooming, buzzing, undifferentiated confusion visual life would be if we all arose tomorrow morning with our attention capable of dwelling only on what had heretofore been completely overlooked. Indeed, our mental institutions are full of poor souls who, despite having normal vision, can observe nothing: theirs is a rhapsodic, kaleidoscopic, senseless barrage of sense signals—answering to nothing, signifying naught.

The physicist's baby and the layman laboratory visitor can see all right; they are not blind. But they cannot see what the physicist sees; they are blind to what he sees. Their eyes are normal but they cannot observe what he observes. We may not hear that the oboe is out of tune, though this will be painfully obvious to the trained musician. An Arab pronunciation of "cat" may clearly indicate a northern dialect to a native; it may be a completely unintelligible noise to us.

(Incidentally, the musician does not hear the raw tones of the oboe and then *interpret* them as being out of tune; he simply hears the oboe to be out of tune. The Arab simply hears the word as indicative of a northern dialect. *We* simply see what time it is (we don't visually remark the position of the clock hands and then clamp horological theories onto the sensations). The surgeon simply observes the wound to be septic; the physicist simply observes the X-ray tube's anode to be overheating.)

The elements of the laboratory visitor's visual field, though singly and severally identical with those of the physicist, are not *organized* for him as they are for the physicist; the lines, colors, and shapes are apprehended by both, but not in the same way. There are indefinitely many ways in which a constellation of lines, shapes and patches may be seen. *Why* a visual pattern is seen differently is a question for experimental psychology. But *that* it may be seen differently is important for any examination of the concepts of *observation* and *interpretation*.

It may be objected "Everyone, whatever his state of knowledge, will see the drawn Necker cube as a box or a cube viewed as from above or as from below." True; in fact almost everyone—infant, layman, physicist—will see the figure as boxlike in one way or another. But could such observations be made by people totally ignorant of the construction of boxlike objects? No. This objection only shows that most of us—the blind, babies, and dimwits excluded—have learned enough to be *able to see* such a figure as a three-dimensional box. This reveals something about the way in which the baby and the physicist *do* see the same thing; that they do in some sense has not really been denied at all. They both see something bright and flashy. When the infant becomes a schoolboy, he and his physicist father will both see the X-ray tube to be breakable and brittle: it will smash if dropped.

Examining how observers see different things in a given physical phenomenon marks something important about when they claim to observe the same thing. If seeing different things involves different knowledge, theories and expectations about X, then their seeing the same thing involves their *sharing* knowledge, theories, and expectations about X. The physicist and his baby share no knowledge of X-ray tubes. They see the same thing only in that if they are looking at X, they are both having *some* visual experience of it. The schoolboy and the physicist agree on more: they see the same thing in a stronger sense. Their visual fields are organized in much the same way; for example, neither observes the X-ray tube about to break out in a grin or about to crack up into ice cubes. (The baby is not visually "set" against even these eventualities.)

6. Only by an examination such as we have just been through is it possible realistically to understand how two scientific observers can encounter the same data, commit themselves to the same descriptive statements, and yet draw diametrically opposed conclusions as to the significance of what they encountered. Thus, before the explicit "theorizing" begins, the issue is still "What are the data?" The simple phenomenalistic formula suggests they took in identical data and then clamped well-developed but different theories onto them. But surely it might be argued that, since their total accounts of what they observed were so radically different, there must be a sense in which they did not begin from the same observational data at all.

Remember, the Necker cube was not the invention of a mischievous psychologist. It dates from 1832, when the Swiss naturalist L. A. Necker described how certain rhomboidal crystals could be microscopically viewed (obliquely) so that their perspective could shift in the now familiar way. One need not work overtime inventing variable perspective and variable aspect figures to establish that observation and interpretation are inextricably intertwined. Such phenomena are to be found daily in the research work of observational microbiologists, X-ray crystallographers, bubble-chamber physicists, and others. A meaningful scientific observation must be of something as something of some kind. This requires appreciation of the data beyond anything a camera or an eyeball is capable of. It requires a scientific observer.

Take a record of an observer's recent observations and begin systematically to decompose it into two lists A and B: in A we cite only the signals filtering through his optical reticulum. In

B we have only the abstract theoretical commitments for which he would argue. *Neither* list, *A* or *B*, can even approximate to constituting genuine scientific observation. *A* will be a chaotic summary of kaleidoscopic encounters with color patches and shapes. *B* will remain unlinked to anything empirical. *A* may be indistinguishable from the inner-life reports of a mescalin addict. *B* could quickly become an exercise in pure mathematics.

The two lists result from something like separating the warp from the woof of a textile fabric—the result being no fabric at all, but simply an array of threads vertical here, horizontal there. Again, one cannot, in principle, heighten the lift on an aircraft wing without generating an "induced drag"—which is but another aspect of that very airflow that produces the lift. Interrupt that flow to separate the drag from the lift and you destroy the lift altogether. The matter and the form of a statue are inseparably intertwined—a point which Aristotle commended to our attention over two millennia ago. By reflections of the same kind observation and interpretation must be seen as inextricably intertwined.

With natural science one can, of course, distinguish those cases of observation wherein theoretical extrapolation dominates the empirical base, from other cases within which the data appear to dominate. But one cannot, cannot in logical principle, go to the limit of considering scientific observation as totally unformed by "significance criteria" or, on the other hand, scientific theories as completely separated from questions of what actually happens.

Hence, scientific observation and scientific interpretation need neither be joined nor separated. They are never apart, so they need not be joined. They cannot, not even in principle, be separated, and it is conceptually idle to make the attempt. Observation and interpretation are related symbiotically so that each conceptually sustains the other, while separation kills both. This will not be news to any practicing scientist, but it may seem heretical indeed to certain philosophers of science for whom *Analysis* has, alas, become indistinguishable from *Division*.

10 PROBABILITY AND CONFIRMATION

Hilary Putnam

The story of deductive logic is well known. Until the beginning of the nineteenth century, deductive logic as a subject was represented by a finite and rather short list of well-known patterns of valid inference. The paucity of the subject did not discourage scholars, however—there were professorships in Logic, courses in Logic, and volumes—fat, fat volumes—in Logic. Indeed, if anyone wants to see just how much can be made out of how little subject matter, I suggest a glance at any nineteenth-century text in traditional logic. The revolution in the subject was brought about by the work of the English logician G. Boole.

Boole's full contribution to the mathematics of his time has still to be fully appreciated. In addition to creating single handed the subject of mathematical logic, he wrote what is still the classic text on the subject of the calculus of finite differences, and he pioneered what are today known as "operator methods" in connection with differential equations. To each of the subjects that he touched—calculus of finite differences, differential equations, logic—he contributed powerful new ideas and an elegant symbolic technique. Since Boole, mathematical logic has never stopped advancing: E. Schröder and Frege extended Boole's work to relations and added quantifiers; H. Behmann solved the decision problem for monadic logic; L. Löwenheim pioneered the subject that is today called "model theory"; Russell extended the system to higher types; and by 1920, the modern period in the history of the subject was in full swing and the stage was set for the epochal results of Gödel and his followers in the 1930's.

The hope naturally arises, therefore, that there might someday be a comparable revolution in *inductive* logic. Inductive logic, too, has a traditional stock of recognized patterns of inference—again a not very long list is all that is involved, notwithstanding the big books on the subject—and the hope is understandable that the mathematical method might be as fruitful in enriching and enlarging this subject as it has been in enriching and enlarging the subject of deductive logic. So far this hope has not been rewarded. However, a number of American philosophers and logicians have been extremely active both in prosecuting the attempt to create a subject of mathematical inductive logic and in criticizing it; and in this essay I will give both a very brief account of the progress that has been made and of the difficulties that have arisen. In the process I hope to give some hint of the extraordinary range and vitality of the discussion that is now taking place in the foundations of scientific methodology.

CARNAP'S SCHOOL

The most important and ambitious attempt to erect a foundation for mathematical inductive logic is due to Rudolf Carnap, who came to the United States as a refugee from Hitler Germany in the 1930's, and who turned to inductive logic in the late 1940's. Although Carnap is now retired from his duties as a professor at the University of California at Los Angeles, he continues to carry on his investigations in this field and has inspired a number of younger logicians to become interested in it. It may be said that Carnap's work has today the sort of importance for the whole field of inductive logic that Frege's work had for deductive logic in the first years of this century: it is obviously unsatisfactory as it stands, but there is no real alternative approach. Either the difficulties with Carnap's approach must be surmounted, or the whole project must be abandoned.

Inductive logic is concerned with the relation of *confirmation*. Just as in deductive logic we consider certain correct inferences which lead from a set of sentences P (called the *premises* of the inference) to a conclusion S, so in inductive logic we deal with certain inferences which lead from a set of sentences E (called the *evidence* for the inductive inference) to a conclusion *S*. The premises of a good deductive inference are said to *imply* the conclusion *S*; the evidence, in the case of a warranted inductive inference, is said to *confirm* the conclusion *S*. The difference in terminology reflects some of the fundamental differences between the two subjects. The most important of these differences is that in a warranted inductive inference the sentences *E* may be true and the conclusion *S* may still be false. It is for this reason that we do not say that *E implies S* but choose the weaker terminology *E confirms S*. This difference has one immediately annoying consequence: it makes it difficult to state with any degree of precision what inductive logic is *about*.

Since deductive inferences are truth-preserving (this means: if the premises are true, the conclusion *must* be true), we can characterize deductive logic by saying that we seek mathematical rules for deriving conclusions from sets of premises which will preserve truth: which will lead from true premises only to true conclusions. But in *inductive* logic we seek what? Mathematical rules which will lead from true premises to conclusions which are *probably* true, relative to those premises. But "probably" in what sense? If all we seek are rules that will be generally successful in the real world as a matter of actual empirical fact, then since the criterion for success is an empirical one, it does not seem very likely that it can be made mathematically precise, or that a precise and powerful mathematical theory of the class of inference-rules with this characteristic can ever be attained. If we seek rules which will lead to conclusions which are probably true on the evidence given in some *a priori* sense of "probably true," then what reason is there to think that there exists a defensible and scientifically interesting *a priori* notion of probability?

Let us bypass these difficulties for the moment by agreeing that, just as in deductive logic there are certain clear cases of valid reasoning, so in inductive logic there are certain clear cases of warranted inductive reasoning, and we can at least attempt to see if these have any mathematically interesting structural properties. The possible gains from a successful system of mathematical inductive logic are so great that we should not refuse even to let the inquiry commence because the relation of confirmation cannot be delineated in advance in a wholly precise way. We shall start, then, with an unanalyzed relation of *confirmation* and see what we might do to make it precise.

Carnap's leading idea is to assume that a *quantitative* measure of confirmation, which he calls *degree* of confirmation, can be worked out. Degrees of confirmation are real numbers between 0 and 1. A degree of confirmation of, say, 7/8 corresponds to a "fair betting quotient" of 7:1, that is, if one were forced to bet on the truth or falsity of S at odds of 7:1, the evidence E being such that the proposition S is confirmed to the degree 7/8, then one should be indifferent whether one's money is placed on S being true or on S being false. If the odds were 6:1 then one should ask that one's money be placed on S; while if the odds were 8:1 then one should ask that one's money be placed on not-S, that is, one should bet that S is false. Thus the odds at which an "ideal inductive judge" would regard it as a matter of indifference whether his money is placed on S or on not-S are determined by and reciprocally determine the exact "degree of confirmation" of S on any evidence E.

Since the idealized "betting situation" just alluded to plays a large role in Carnap's thinking, it is necessary to examine it more closely. The situation is obviously unrealistic in numerous respects. For example, if the bet concerns the truth or falsity of a scientific *theory*, then how should the bet ever be decided? Even if we can agree to call the theory *false* in certain definite cases, under what circumstances would we decide that the theory was certainly *true* and that the money should be paid to the affirmative bettor?

Even if we assume that we have available an "oracle" who decides all of our bets for us, and by whose decisions we are willing to abide, is it reasonable to assume that even an *ideal* inductive judge could have such a thing as a *total* betting strategy which would enable him to assign *exact* "fair betting quotients" in all possible evidential situations and to all possible hypotheses? This question is connected with the reasonableness of the "subjective probability" notion, to which we shall come later. Suppose, finally, that we assume that an "ideal inductive judge" could always arrive at a set of odds which he regarded as "fair" in connection with any S, and given any evidence E. Is it reasonable to suppose that this judgment could be independent of both his empirical knowledge and the hypotheses he is clever enough to frame?

These questions may be answered in the following way. What we seek, following Carnap, is a precise definition of a "c-function"—a function $c(E,S)$ whose first argument is a sentence (or more generally a set of sentences), whose second argument is a sentence, and whose values are real numbers between 0 and 1 which can be used to guide our betting, and, more generally, our beliefs and actions, in the following way: if $c(E,S)$ has the value p/q, we shall take odds on S of p:q-p as "fair," and adjust our expectations accordingly. If such a function c can be constructed, and the function c turns out to "learn from experience" and to "predict" more cleverly than any existing inductive judge (or as well as the best existing inductive judges), then we shall certainly be highly satisfied.

If the notion of "fair odds" is indeed vague in many situations, in connection with many hypotheses S, we can then *make* it precise by defining the odds p:q-p to be fair, where $p/q = c(E,S)$. Such a function c would then determine a *total* betting strategy in the sense just described. How reasonable it is to hope for such a thing we cannot determine in advance: who in 1850 could have anticipated the evolution of deductive logic in the next hundred years? If the judgments of an inductive judge are based not just on the evidence E but on collateral information E' available to him, we may insist that this evidence E' be explicitly formulated, that is, that the degree of confirmation be computed not on the basis of E but on the basis of $E\&E'$ (this is called the *requirement of total evidence* in inductive logic). And the function c will, of course, "consider" all hypotheses that can be framed in the language. The development of new theoretical languages may modify our inductive predictions, but within a fixed scientific language we hope for an adequate function c, with respect to the hypotheses that can be framed in that language and the evidence that can be expressed in that language.

Space does not permit me to go further into Carnap's approach than these introductory remarks. The details may be found in Carnap's book *Logical Foundations of Probability* and in his monograph *The Continuum of Inductive Methods*.

THE DIAGONAL ARGUMENT

Carnap's published work has so far considered only hypotheses *S* and evidence *E* of a very simple and highly restricted kind. In particular, Carnap does not consider problems involving *sequential orderings*. For example, the evidence might be that 200 balls have been drawn from an urn and of these 162 were red and the remainder not-red, but not that every *third* ball (in some sequence) is red, nor would the hypothesis be that every third ball will continue to be red.

The difficulty is not just a difficulty with Carnap's notation. Carnap's "*c*-functions" are defined over languages which contain names for relations (for example, "to the left of") as well as properties ("red," "square," "hard"). Thus we can express the fact that every third ball of the balls so far drawn has been red in Carnap's notation by introducing a primitive relation symbol *R* which is to be interpreted in such a way that *Rab* means "ball *a* is drawn before ball *b*." Using the symbol *R* and the usual logical symbols we *can* then say that so-and-so-many balls have been drawn and every third one has been red, and we can also express the prediction that, say, the next two balls to be drawn will be not-red and the third one will again be red. But it then turns out that Carnap's *c*-functions assign a probability of about one-third to the hypothesis that any future ball will be red independently of its position in the sequence of drawings. In other words, Carnap's inductive logics are clever enough, if we think of them as mechanical learning devices, to "learn from experience" that approximately one-third of the balls drawn have a certain non-relational property, but they are not "clever enough" to learn that position in the sequence is relevant.

Since this point is crucial to the whole discussion, let me emphasize it somewhat. As I have already indicated, we may think of a system of inductive logic as a design for a "learning machine": that is to say, a design for a computing machine that can extrapolate certain kinds of empirical regularities from the data with which it is supplied. Then the criticism of the so-far-constructed "*c*-functions" is that they correspond to "learning machines" of very low power. They can extrapolate the simplest possible empirical generalizations, for example: "approximately nine-tenths of the balls are red," but they cannot extrapolate so simple a regularity as "every other ball is red." Suppose now that we had a sequence with a regularity that required the exercise of a high order of intelligence to discover. For instance, all the balls up to a certain point might be red, and from that point on the second (after the point in question) might be black, also the third, also the fifth . . . and, in general, all the balls at a *prime* place in the sequence (counting from the point in question) might be black, while the balls at a composite place in the sequence might be red. Needless to say, a "learning machine," or an inductive logic that could extrapolate *such* a regularity is not today in existence. The question is whether such a thing will ever exist.

One difficulty with Carnap's program is this: to say that a certain prediction—say, "the next ball will be red and the one after that will be black"—is highly confirmed on the evidence given implies that, considering all *possible* hypotheses as to the regularity governing the sequence, this is the *best* prediction one can make. If there is such a thing as a correct definition of "degree of confirmation" which can be fixed once and for all, then a machine which predicted in accordance with the degree of confirmation would be an *optimal*, that is to say, a cleverest possible learning machine. Thus any argument against the existence of a cleverest possible learning machine must show either that Carnap's program cannot be completely fulfilled or that the correct *c*-function must be one that cannot be computed by a machine. Either conclusion would be of interest.

The first alternative says, in effect, that inductive logic cannot be formalized in Carnap's way—on the basis of a quantitative notion of degree of confirmation; while the second alternative says that inductive logic must be a highly non-constructive theory: that is, it may *define* in some way the concept "best possible prediction on given evidence," but the definition cannot be applied mechanically; rather we will have to hire a mathematician to try to *prove* that a given prediction is "best possible" on the basis of the definition, and, since we cannot give the mathematician a uniform rule for finding such proofs, we have no guarantee that he will succeed in any given case.

Of course, neither alternative would be wholly fatal to Carnap's program. If the first alternative is correct, we can still try to construct better and better learning machines, even if we cannot hope to build, or even give precise sense to the notion of a "best possible" one. And if the second alternative is correct, we can always *say* that any precise and correct mathematical definition of "degree of confirmation" would be of interest, even if degree of confirmation does not turn out to be a function that a computing machine can compute, even when S is as simple as "the next ball will be red and the one after that will be black," and E is merely a record of past drawings from an urn.

Is there, then, an argument against the existence—that is, against the possible existence—of a "cleverest possible" learning machine? The answer is that there is. The argument appears in detail in a paper of mine in *The Philosophy of Rudolf Carnap*, but the leading idea is very simple. Let T be any learning machine, and consider what T predicts if the first, second, . . . and so on balls are all red. Sooner or later (if T is not hopelessly weak as a learning device) there must come an n such that T predicts "the nth ball will be red." Call this number n_1. If we let n_1 be black, and then the next ball after that be red, and the next after that again be red, and so on, then two things can happen. T's confidence may have been so shaken by the failure of its prediction at n_1 that T refuses to ever again predict that a future ball will be red. In this case we make all the rest of the balls red. Then the regularity "all the balls with finitely many exceptions are red" is a very simple regularity that T fails to extrapolate. So T is certainly not a "cleverest possible" learning device.

On the other hand, it can happen (and in fact it will, if T has any power as a learning machine at all), that, in spite of its failure on n_1, T "regains confidence," and, if all the balls after n_1 have been red for a long time, T finally predicts "the next ball will be red." Call this next place in the sequence n_2 and make that ball black. Continuing in this way, we can effectively calculate an infinite sequence of numbers n_1, n_2, . . . such that if we make all the balls red *except* the ones at n_1, n_2, . . . and make *those* black, then we will *defeat* the machine T. That is, we will have constructed a regularity, depending on T, which it is beyond the power of T to extrapolate.

However, I have proved that it is always possible to build another machine which can extrapolate every regularity that T can extrapolate and also extrapolate the one that T *can't* extrapolate. Thus, there cannot be a "cleverest possible" learning machine: for, for every learning machine T, there exists a machine T' which can learn everything that T can learn and more besides. This sort of argument is called a *diagonal argument* by logicians. Applied to inductive logic it yields the conclusion I stated before: that either there are better and better c-functions, but no "best possible," or else there is a "best possible" but it is not computable by a machine, even when S and E are restricted to the sorts of situations we have been considering —that is, drawing balls from an urn, noting their color, and trying to predict the color of future balls.

CONFIRMATION OF UNIVERSAL LAWS

It is possible that some of my readers who have mathematical training may wish to explore this fascinating field of inductive logic themselves. They can certainly do so. The field is still in its infancy, and no special knowledge is needed to enter at this point beyond what is contained in Carnap's book. However, I should like to make a suggestion or two as to what might be fruitful lines for future investigation.

Carnap's approach in his detailed investigations has been to consider languages over finite universes—say, a "universe" consisting of 300 balls of various colors in an urn. Once degree of confirmation has been defined for a universe with N objects, for arbitrary N, Carnap extends the definition to languages over an infinite universe by a limiting process. The restriction is imposed: when S and E are statements about finitely many explicitly mentioned individuals, that is, when S and E do not contain the words "all" and "some," then the degree of confirmation of S on E must not depend on N (the number of individuals in the language). Carnap calls this requirement the *requirement of fitting together,* and so far it has played a rather unhappily restricting role in inductive logic. As already mentioned, the methods so far constructed have extremely low "learning power," and I suspect that this is connected with this way of proceeding from such highly restricted cases.

A method that would appear more natural to a mathematician used to working with continuous functions and spaces would be this: start with a language over a universe with continuously many individuals (say, space-time points), and whose primitive notions are continuous functions. The possible worlds, or "state descriptions," as Carnap calls them, relative to this language, would then form a continuous space. Each c-function would be a (presumably continuous) function over this space with an infinitesimal value on each state description.

If, now, there is a reason for defining degree of confirmation on some universe with only N individuals, for some finite n, we can do this by identifying those N individuals with N arbitrarily chosen individuals in the infinite world. In other words, instead of extending our c-function from the finite languages to the infinite language as Carnap does, we extend it from the infinite language to the various finite languages. In this way the "requirement of fitting together" will automatically be met. Also, another serious difficulty in Carnap's approach disappears. Carnap's methods, in the monograph *The Continuum of Inductive Methods,* assign to a universal law the degree of confirmation *zero* in the limit, that is, as N approaches infinity.

In other words, the probability (in an infinite universe) that a universal law holds without exception is strictly zero on any finite amount of evidence. In a certain sense, then, strictly universal laws cannot be extrapolated at all: we can only extrapolate laws of the form "99 per cent of all individuals conform to the law L." However, if we start directly with the infinite universe, there is no difficulty in constructing a c-function which assigns a specified universal law S the probability .90 on evidence E. We simply have to assign our infinitesimal degree of confirmation to each state description in which S holds and E also holds in such a way that the degree of confirmation of S on E (integrated over all state descriptions of the kind just mentioned) is .90. Indeed, given any initial measure function c_0 which does *not* permit the extrapolation of the law S, and given evidence E from which we wish to extrapolate S, we can easily *modify* c_0 so that on evidence E the degree of confirmation of S will be .90, while on evidence incompatible with E all degrees of confirmation remained unaltered. This idea is used in the proof that given a function c_0 we can construct a function c_1 which will extrapolate every regularity that c_0 will extrapolate and also some regularity that c_0 won't extrapolate.

SIMPLICITY ORDERINGS

In a recent interesting book, Jerrold Katz reviews the notion of a *simplicity ordering*, first introduced into inductive logic by John Kemeny, who proved some interesting theorems about these orderings and their influence on inductive methods. A simplicity ordering is just what the name implies: an ordering H_1, H_2, H_3, H_4, . . . of hypotheses in order of decreasing simplicity or increasing complexity, by some measure of "simplicity." Katz emphasizes that any inductive method implicitly determines a simplicity ordering. For, on any given E, there will be infinitely many mutually incompatible hypotheses which are compatible with E. Suppose S_1, S_2 are two such hypotheses and we regard S_1 as highly confirmed. Since S_2 was also in agreement with E, why did we not regard S_2 as highly confirmed? We may say "because S_1 was so much simpler than S_2." But this is "simplicity after the fact." We *call* S_1 simpler than S_2 *because* it is the hypothesis to which we assign the high degree of confirmation.

More precisely: we may *either* suppose that the simplicity ordering is given first, and then it is determined that S_1 is to be preferred over S_2 for reasons of "simplicity," *or* we may suppose that the c-function is given first, and then the simplicity ordering is determined by which we prefer. In general, evidence E cannot confirm a hypothesis S unless E is incompatible with every hypothesis S' such that S' is simpler than S. If a learning machine T is incapable of extrapolating a hypothesis S at all, then this means that S is not located in the simplicity ordering of hypotheses that can be confirmed by T at all. If T is based on a c-function, then to "improve" T so that T will become able to confirm S what we have to do is modify the function c so that S becomes confirmed on suitable evidence E without destroying the ability of T to confirm other hypotheses when the evidence is incompatible with S. We have, so to speak, to "insert" S into the simplicity ordering of the hypotheses confirmable by T.

A problem which, therefore, has considerable importance for inductive logic is this: given a simplicity ordering of some hypotheses, to construct a c-function which will be in agreement with that simplicity ordering, that is, which will permit one to extrapolate any one of these hypotheses, and which will give the preference always to the earliest hypothesis in the ordering which is compatible with the data. I believe that this problem should not be too difficult to solve, and that its solution may provide an impetus for a new way of constructing c-functions in inductive logic.

One result which is of interest is this: If we require that any two hypotheses in a simplicity ordering must lead to different predictions, then it can be shown by techniques which are due to Gödel that *no* simplicity ordering can include all possible hypotheses and be such that we can effectively list the hypotheses in that order by using a computing machine. If we call an ordering "effective" provided that a computing machine could be programmed to produce the hypotheses in question according to that ordering, then this says that no effective simplicity ordering can contain *all* hypotheses. Thus we can construct "better and better"—that is, more and more inclusive—simplicity orderings, but there is no "best" effective simplicity ordering. The program that I am suggesting, of starting with simplicity orderings and constructing c-functions, would therefore lead to a sequence of "better and better" c-functions—that is, to inductive logics of greater and greater learning power—but not to an "optimal"

111

c-function. But this does not seem to be a serious drawback, to me anyway, since an "optimal *c*-function is hardly something to be hoped for.

SUBJECTIVE PROBABILITY AND COHERENCE

A *c*-function may also be interpreted as a measure of the degree to which a person with evidence E gives credence to a hypothesis S. On this interpretation, *c*-functions are just "subjective probability metrics" of the kind studied by I. J. Good, L. J. Savage, B. de Finetti, and others of the "subjective probability" school. The difference between Carnap's approach and that of, say, de Finetti is that de Finetti claimed to be studying *actual* belief whereas Carnap explicitly says that he is studying *rational* belief, that is, the belief or betting system of an idealized inductive judge (or a "learning machine"). A *c*-function is called *coherent* if there does not exist a finite system of bets that events $e_1, \ldots, e_n$ will occur, with stakes $s_1, \ldots, s_n$, and odds which are fair according to the function c, such that if the amounts $s_1, \ldots, s_n$ are wagered on the events $e_1, \ldots, e_n$ respectively at the respective odds, then no matter which of the events occur and which do not occur, the bettor must lose money.

In other words, if your *c*-function is incoherent, then there exists a system of bets which I can invite you to make which is such that you *must* lose money if you make those bets, and yet the bets are "fair" according to your own subjective probability system. It has been proved by F. P. Ramsey, de Finetti, and Kemeny that a *c*-function is coherent if and only if it is a normalized probability metric, that is, if and only if it obeys the usual axioms of the mathematic theory of probability. A stronger requirement of *strict coherence* has been introduced by Shimony, and has been shown to be equivalent to the requirement that the *c*-function must not assign the values o and 1 themselves to propositions which are neither logically false nor logically true.

In my opinion the requirements of coherence must be taken *cum grano salis.* Consider a total betting system which includes the rule: if it is ever shown that a hypothesis S is not included in the simplicity ordering corresponding to the betting system at time t, where t is the time in question, then modify the betting system so as to "insert" the hypothesis S at a place n corresponding to one's intuitive judgment of the "complexity" of the hypothesis S. This rule violates two principles imposed by Carnap. First of all, it violates the rule that if one changes one's degrees of confirmation in one's life, then this should be wholly accounted for by the change in E, that is the underlying c-function itself must not be changed. Secondly, it can easily be shown that even if one's bets at any one time are coherent, one's total betting strategy through time will not be coherent. But there is no doubt that this is a good rule nonetheless, and that one would be foolish not to improve one's c-function whenever one can. For we are not playing against a malevolent opponent but against nature, and nature does not exploit such "incoherencies"; and even if we *were* playing against a malevolent opponent, there are many ways to lose one's "bets" besides being "incoherent."

CONCLUSION

In this chapter I have stressed the idea that the task of inductive logic is the construction of a "universal learning machine." Present-day inductive logics are learning devices of very low power. But this is no reason for alarm: rather we should be excited that such devices have been designed, even if they have very low power, and optimistic about the likelihood of their future improvement. In the future, the development of a powerful mathematical theory of inductive inference, of "machines that learn," and of better mathematical models for human learning may all grow out of this enterprise.

Carnap was driven from Germany by Hitler, and his position has been condemned in the Soviet Union as "subjective idealism." Even in the United States there have been a great many who could not understand this attempt to turn philosophy into a scientific discipline with substantive scientific results, and who have been led to extreme and absurd misinterpretations of the work I have reported to you in this essay. Few, perhaps, would have expected traditional empiricism to lead to the development of a speculative theory of "universal learning machines"; and yet, in retrospect, a concern with systematizing inductive logic has been the oldest concern of empiricist philosophers from Bacon on. No one can yet predict the outcome of this speculative scientific venture. But it is amply clear, whether this particular venture succeeds or fails, that the toleration of philosophical and scientific speculation brings rich rewards and that its suppression leads to sterility.

11 UTILITY AND ACCEPTANCE OF HYPOTHESES

Isaac Levi

We are apt to think of the scientist as someone quite different from the policy maker. Unlike the man of action, the scientist is concerned not with what we ought to do but with what we ought to believe. His aim is to make true predictions, to describe past and present as accurately as he can, and to explain what he predicts and describes in terms of general laws and theories. Moreover, in his quest for truth the scientist must overcome his personal prejudices. Even his moral commitments and the interests of the society or the group which he serves should not interfere with his conclusions.

Unlike the policy maker, the scientist is supposed to observe neutrality on questions of value. This does not mean that he must be cold-blooded. Nor does it imply that he must avoid value commitments in determining what problems he will select for study. But once he has chosen a problem, value neutrality requires that he determine which of the possible answers is correct on the evidence available to him independently of his value commitments.

Consider an economic adviser to the President of the United States. As a scientist, he is obligated to study the consequences of various types of economic policy and to reach conclusions without regard for his values, for the President's values, or for the interests of the American people. How can the results he obtains be applied to a practical problem such as whether to reduce taxes?

The obvious and classical answer to this question is that when choosing between alternative courses of action (for example, a tax cut and increased government spending), the policy maker must know his goals and values and also know the consequences for his goals of adopting one or another alternative policy. Furnishing the goals and values is not within the province of the scientist as a disinterested investigator of the truth. He does, however, play a legitimate role in determining the consequences of the various policies. This he can do in the course of his disinterested quest for truth. Thus, although the aim of the scientist is to seek the truth, the conclusions which he reaches in his theoretical inquiries often furnish information about consequences of vital importance to the decision maker.

All of this seems too obvious to be worth discussing. But closer scrutiny indicates certain difficulties. Notice that the scientist cannot guarantee to the policy maker that his predictions will be borne out. Nothing is certain, not even death and taxes. The evidence on which conclusions in the natural and social sciences are based can at best confirm these conclusions to a degree. They are more or less probable. The traditional account assumes that the policy maker relies on the predictions which the scientist accepts as true. This is wrong. A rational decision maker relies not on these predictions but on the probability that they are correct.

Consider a man suffering from an ailment for which either a drug therapy or surgery is recommended. The drug therapy offers a 50–50 chance of cure, whereas surgery offers a 70 per cent chance of success. Assume also that failure in both cases does not change the patient's condition appreciably.

The physician, like the President's economist, must be both a scientist and a decision maker. As a decision maker he must take into account the values and the interests of his patient. In this, the classical view is correct, but it is mistaken in contending that the physician as scientist contributes to the decision by making predictions as to what will happen if either of the treatments is adopted. Making a prediction is tantamount to accepting a certain statement as true. In the circumstances just described, no responsible physician could make a prediction as to the outcome of either drug therapy or surgery. At best, he could give some indication of the probabilities of the truth of various predictions. Consequently, as a decision maker, the physician cannot rely on predictions as to what will happen but only on the probabilities that it will happen.

Suppose that chance of cure by surgery was 98 per cent instead of 70 per cent, but that failure of surgery would result in death. As a scientist interested in the truth, the physician might feel warranted in predicting success, but as a policy maker he might recommend the drug therapy, for the consequences of failure with the drug therapy are so much less serious than they are in the case of surgery. Thus, even when the scientist can make predictions, these predictions are irrelevant to deciding on a course of action. What is relevant is the degree to which the evidence supports the prediction. When a human life is at stake, our ethical commitments often require higher probabilities for *action* than for *belief*.

The traditional view is indeed correct in distinguishing between the practical and the theoretical aims of science. But it is mistaken in holding that the results of furthering theoretical aims contribute to the realization of practical goals. What the scientist contributes to policy making is found not in the conclusions of his inquiries but in the probabilities on which these conclusions are based.

Although men have long recognized that all decision making involves risks, only in recent years have there been widespread sustained attempts to formulate in a systematic way principles of rational decision making which take into account probabilities of success and failure as well as the values or utilities of the decision maker. Jeremy Bentham, at the end of the eighteenth century, suggested that a rational decision maker should maximize utility, and that in so doing he should take probabilities into account. But for Bentham utility was a measure of pleasure and pain. Unfortunate choice; not only have there been serious difficulties with assigning numerical values to pleasure and pain, but it is at least debatable whether men ought to make the maximizing of pleasure and the minimizing of pain their sole objective.

The distinguished mathematician John von Neumann has shown how the notion of utility could be extricated from these difficulties by constructing a notion of utility that may be used to measure value where value involves moral and political considerations as well as personal preferences, pain, pleasure, and so on. Together with his economist colleague, Oskar Morgenstern, von Neumann developed the foundations of a mathematical theory of games and indicated how it might be applied to economic decisions.

Statisticians such as Jerzy Neyman, Abraham Wald, and Leonard Savage have attempted to recast the central questions of statistics as problems in decision making. R. B. Braithwaite, the British philosopher, has argued that the game theory has relevance for questions of ethics. These writers and many other statisticians, economists, sociologists, and philosophers, all of whom have some interest in rational action, have contributed to a growing body of literature on game and decision theory. Much of this material is covered in the excellent critical survey *Games and Decisions,* by D. Luce and H. Raiffa.

We cannot discuss the results contributed by decision theory to the understanding of rational policy making here, but one elementary idea which underlies much of the work in this field is important. Let us return to the decision facing the doctor who has a choice between surgery and drug therapy when treating a disease. How is he to decide between them? Should he take into account only the probability of successful cure and opt for the policy which promises the greater chance of success?

If the consequences of failure are no more disastrous when surgery is selected than when drugs are, this would be reasonable. But if failure of surgery is fatal whereas failure of the drug therapy is not, the probability of success through surgery ought to be much higher than probability of success through drugs before surgery is chosen. Making a decision is like gambling (although it is much less frivolous): If the losses to be sustained are very high, the chances of success must be high before a rational man will take the risk.

Let us assume, for the sake of the argument, that decision theory can help us understand in detail how the probabilities furnished by the scientist contribute to deciding how to act. We must now ask how these probabilities help promote the scientist's own attempt to replace doubt by true belief.

Probabilities, after all, are just as important to the scientist as they are to the policy maker. Like the policy maker who takes a risk that his actions may prove unsuccessful in furthering his goals, the scientist who accepts a certain answer to a given question as true takes a risk that his answer may be in error. Hence, as in the case of decision making, there is a need for criteria for determining how high the probability of success (and how low the probability of error) must be before a scientist can accept a given answer as true.

Many critics have argued that this problem cannot be solved unless the alleged value neutrality of the scientist is abandoned. According to these critics, the only way in which minimum probabilities for accepting propositions as true can be determined is by taking into account the values or utilities of the investigator or of the community whose interests he serves. Like the decision maker, the scientist must take into account the seriousness of mistakes in determining minimum probabilities.

This argument against value neutrality will not stand by itself. It rests on a misconception of what scientific value neutrality entails. When a person decides to engage in scientific activity, he perforce commits himself to certain values. He obligates himself never to accept contradictions as true, never to accept assertions from uncertified authorities, and, in general, to conform to certain principles governing when it is and when it is not legitimate to accept propositions on the basis of given evidence. A commitment to a scientific way of doing things is a value commitment which no reasonable interpretation of value neutrality can prohibit. But once the scientist has committed himself to drawing conclusions in accordance with the canons of scientific inquiry, he can be forbidden to take into account any other value commitments he might have. This is the prohibition implied by scientific value neutrality.

Thus, although we do need to decide on minimum probabilities for accepting scientific conclusions, these minima may be determined by the canons of scientific inquiry in a standard way which the scientist is not permitted to alter to suit his own tastes or values. This situation would be compatible with value neutrality.

Throughout this discussion we have assumed that, in addition to its contribution to decision making, science has a concern of its own—to wit, seeking the truth. This view has been subject to serious doubt on the basis of considerations deriving from recent theories of statistical method. According to views developed by several contemporary writers on statistical theory, the fundamental problem of statistics is what Neyman calls "inductive behavior."

A manufacturer's decision to market a given product might depend in part on whether the quality of the product is sufficiently high. If too many defects are found in a sample subject to inspection he might withhold the product. The effectiveness of drugs and vaccines, educational programs and so forth are frequently tested through the use of techniques of statistical inference. In all these cases—and many more—the aim of statistical method is to provide information concerning probabilities which will be relevant to rational action in the face of uncertainty where the seriousness of error is important. According to this conception, statistics is nothing but a special branch of decision theory.

But here a difficulty arises. The same techniques that are designed to handle decisions how to act in the face of uncertainty are also employed in deciding what to believe. In genetics, sociology, and psychology, statistical methods are used to test the truth of scientific hypotheses. Thus, a psychologist may be interested in discovering whether achievements on certain intelligence tests are correlated with specific mental disorders—not, so it would seem, in order to undertake any program of action but solely in an effort to understand mental disorders and performance on intelligence tests. But statistical theory requires that we take into consideration the seriousness of mistakes. This makes sense when we apply statistical theory to inductive behavior—deciding how to act. Does it make sense when statistical theory is applied to the psychologist's problem, which involves inductive inference—deciding what to believe?

Perhaps the answer is that there are two different types of

statistical theory: one for inductive behavior and one for inductive inference. This answer will not do. The statistical methods designed for decision making are also allegedly appropriate in situations which seem to call for accepting or rejecting propositions. Indeed, some of these methods (for example, tests of significance) are actually applied to problems of inductive inference as well as to situations involving inductive behavior. How are we to justify the extrapolation—from deciding how to act to deciding what to believe?

The answer given by many authors takes one of two forms both of which involve a radical rejection of the conception of science which we have been discussing. According to one formulation (the behavioralist view), when a scientist accepts a conclusion as true, he is doing nothing more than acting or being prepared to act as if the proposition were true relative to some practical aim. Thus, to accept as true the claim that the Sabin vaccine will prevent polio is tantamount to being prepared to use it in mass inoculation programs. According to behavioralism, scientists have no special theoretical objectives. The aims of their inquiries are the aims of the policy maker. Indeed, the scientist is a policy maker.

According to a slightly different view, the scientist does not accept or reject propositions at all. He merely indicates how well the available evidence confirms or disconfirms hypotheses. His activity is important because it furnishes the policy maker with probabilities relevant to rational decision. But he has no special theoretical objectives of his own. In sum, the scientist is viewed neither as a man in search of the truth, nor as a decision maker, but as a guidance counselor.

The guidance counselor and behavioralist conceptions of science (which number among their supporters philosophers of the eminence of Carnap and Braithwaite) agree on one important point: whether scientists accept or reject hypotheses, they do so only in a sense equivalent to acting or being prepared to act relative to practical objectives. Consequently, inductive inference *is* inductive behavior. There is no need, therefore, to provide a rationale for applications of statistical methods designed for decision making to cases where we want to decide what to believe, for deciding what to believe is equivalent to deciding how to act.

The reduction of the theoretical aims of science to practical aims is not entirely new. In a way, this view has found expression in the writings of Marx, Bergson, James, Dewey, and others. What is novel is the defense of this reduction by an appeal to statistics and decision theory.

We shall not have the opportunity to consider the many serious difficulties with a behavioralist or guidance counselor conception of science. It will be sufficient to remember that when scientists consider the principle of parity, ask whether the universe is expanding, or inquire whether Galileo actually conducted the celebrated experiment at Pisa, they have practical objectives in mind. To be sure, believing, disbelieving, and doubting may be acts in some broad sense. But the act of believing or accepting a proposition as true is not, at least so it would seem, reducible to overt behavior as the behavioralists suggest. And, as the examples just cited illustrate, scientists appear to accept and reject propositions counter to the guidance counselor view.

However, even if we find the behavioralist and guidance counselor conceptions of science unacceptable, we are still faced with the problem these views attempt to solve—namely, how is it possible to justify applying statistical procedures designed for rational decision making to deciding what to believe?

An idea of the sort of answer that may prove successful can be obtained from the following considerations: even if believing is not the same as acting or being prepared to act, deciding what to believe may be sufficiently similar to deciding how to act to warrant using similar principles to characterize both rational action and rational belief without identifying the two. The situation is comparable to using similar mathematical formulae to characterize the forces due to electrical charge and due to gravity even though electrical charge and gravitational mass are not the same. If such an analogy between deciding what to believe and deciding how to act can be found, then the desired justification of the application of statistical procedures in theoretically oriented inquiries can be obtained without resort either to behavioralism or to the guidance counselor view.

We cannot explore the analogy in detail here, but the following points of similarity can be readily understood. First, when a person is engaged in a scientific inquiry and is considering several possible answers, the investigation terminates with his choosing one of the answers or suspending judgment. In this sense a scientist chooses what to believe just as a policy maker chooses how to act. Second, just as rational policy making is controlled by the goals of the policy maker, scientific inquiry aims at the realization of its own characteristic goals. These theoretical objectives may be characterized as the results of successful efforts to replace doubt by true belief. Third, just as the policy maker risks failing to attain his objective, so does the scientist, for the evidence available to him cannot guarantee the truth of his conclusions but only make them more or less probable. Fourth, just as the goals of the decision maker determine the value or utility to be assigned to the various possible consequences of his actions, so the aims of scientific inquiry determine the "epistemic" utilities of the possible successes and failures of accepting various answers.

Thus, a scientist will prefer a correct answer to an incorrect one. And in many instances a scientist will prefer that one answer be true rather than another. This is especially so when the scientist is looking for explanations which, according to a widely held view, are better if they are simple rather than complex. In such situations the epistemic utility of accepting a true simple answer is higher than that of accepting a true complex answer. Similarly, the disutility of a false simple answer is lower than that of a false complex answer. Finally, we may say with some measure of plausibility that the scientist takes into account the scientific seriousness of error as determined by the epistemic disutility of accepting a false answer.

Of course, in this connection we must remember one important difference between science and decision making. Epistemic utilities and disutilities differ from practical ones in that they do not reflect the personal value commitments of the scientist or those of any group whose interests he serves, with one exception: they do involve a commitment to a scientific mode of inquiry. Thus, as we have noted, the similarities between decision making and the quest for truth do not preclude imposition of a value neutrality requirement on the scientist.

The points of analogy between deciding how to act and deciding what to believe suggest that we may be able to justify applying the principles formulated by contemporary statistical decision theory not only to inductive behavior but also to inductive inference. We cannot begin to consider all of the philosophical and technical problems which must be faced before a final verdict can be rendered on this suggestion. However, if the verdict should prove favorable, it would support a conception of the relation between theory and practice which differs not only from behavioralism and the guidance counselor position but also from the traditional view discussed at the beginning of this chapter.

This position holds, counter to the traditional view, that the results of a scientific quest for truth do not, strictly speaking, contribute to the process of rational decision. The results are propositions which are accepted as true. As we have seen, the decision maker must rely not on the truth of these propositions but on the probabilities of their truth. These probabilities are also needed by the scientist in deciding what to believe. He uses them as a tool just as the decision maker does.

The mistake of the guidance counselor view is the claim that the sole aim of science is to furnish these probabilities for use by the decision maker, whereas the mistake of the behavioralist view is the assumption that the scientist is a decision maker. Science is not the handmaiden of practice nor is it identical with practice. It has its own objectives. Nevertheless, in the pursuit of truth, the scientist does produce, as a byproduct of his own efforts, information which the decision maker, be he ruler of state, industrialist, or average man, ignores only to his own detriment.

12 SPACE AND TIME

Adolf Grünbaum

Among the advances of science that have been of epoch-making importance for philosophy, the development of theories of space and time occupies a conspicuous place.

In this essay I shall present a survey of three such momentous theories as follows: First, I shall give an account of the philosophical significance of the nineteenth-century mathematical discovery of two kinds of geometries, each of which is logically incompatible with Euclid's time-honored set of geometric postulates; next, I shall explain how the findings of physical theories enabled us to see that the time of our universe derives its character from the particular kinds of processes which obtain in the world; and, finally, I shall outline the precise, often misunderstood manner in which the repudiation of earlier physical assumptions prompted Einstein's revision of the concept of simultaneity.

Let me begin with *"non*-Euclidean" geometries. It was not until the nineteenth century that mathematicians became fully aware of the logical possibility of systems of geometric axioms which were each logically incompatible with Euclidean geometry while being no less internally consistent than Euclid's system of postulates. These non-Euclidean geometries then became important in physics with the advent of Einstein's general theory of relativity in 1916.

The impetus for investigations which issued in the realization that *non*-Euclidean geometries are logically possible was provided by inquiring whether Euclid's Fifth Postulate (the so-called

"Parallel Postulate") is deducible from Euclid's first four postulates as a theorem. Euclid defined parallel lines as coplanar straight lines which do *not* intersect, however far produced in either direction. This definition of the word "parallel" must be carefully distinguished from Euclid's Parallel *Postulate,* which states the following: If the sum of the interior angles formed by two straight lines on the same side of a transversal is *less* than 180°, then the two straight lines will intersect on that side of the transversal, thereby *not* being parallel. In the context of the first four of Euclid's postulates, this Fifth Postulate, which we shall call "P_5," can be expressed equivalently as follows: Through a point outside a straight line, *exactly one* line can be drawn parallel to and coplanar with the given straight line. I repeat: Euclid's P_5 asserts the existence of a unique parallel.

A staggering amount of intellectual effort, expended over a period of about two thousand years, failed to yield a proof that P_5 is deducible as a theorem from the first four postulates, which are known collectively as "Absolute Geometry." And this failure to deduce P_5 as a theorem from Absolute Geometry suggested, though it did not prove, that this deduction is *not* logically possible. But, if P_5 is thus not a theorem of Absolute Geometry, then a *logically* consistent system of postulates can be formed by combining Absolute Geometry with a suitable *denial* of Euclid's P_5, the resulting system being a non-Euclidean type of geometry.

If we recall that Euclid's P_5 asserts the existence of a unique parallel, it becomes evident that the denial of P_5 can take either one of two forms, as follows: (1) more than one parallel can be drawn through an exterior point, or (2) no parallel can be drawn through an exterior point.

Upon being confronted with these two ways of denying P_5, the reader may object at once that his imagination boggles at the attempt to picture either of them physically. But this pictorial difficulty arises from the misguided attempt to use the straight lines on (infinitely extended) classroom blackboards or table tops in an effort to visualize the claims about parallelism made by either of the two denials of P_5. The failure of this visualization effort should not occasion any surprise. For the familiar straight lines and angles on surfaces like blackboards exemplify Euclidean geometry and hence cannot simultaneously exemplify the denials of P_5 belonging to corresponding species of non-Euclidean geometry. We shall soon see, however, that even our ordinary physical environment does present us with two other kinds of surfaces which can respectively furnish physical exemplifications of the two species of non-Euclidean geometries generated by the two ways of denying P_5.

It must be pointed out that the denial of P_5 in the form that there are no parallels at all cannot be consistently combined with Absolute Geometry to yield a species of non-Euclidean geometry. This combination would not be feasible logically, because, as can be shown, Absolute Geometry alone entails the theorem that *at least* one parallel can be drawn. Hence a necessary condition for having a kind of non-Euclidean geometry in which there are no parallels at all is that suitable modifications be made in Absolute Geometry as well. By contrast, Absolute Geometry *can* be consistently combined with the assumption that *more than one parallel* can be drawn to form a system of non-Euclidean geometry known as "Hyperbolic Geometry." For Absolute Geometry does *not* entail that there is only *one* parallel but does entail that *at least* one parallel can be drawn. And thus Absolute Geometry *allows* the addition of the assumption that *more* than one parallel can be drawn, an assumption which we shall call the "Hyperbolic Parallel Postulate."

As for a physical visualization of hyperbolic non-Euclidean geometry, the Italian geometer Beltrami discovered that there exists a model of the postulates of plane hyperbolic geometry on a saddle-shaped surface of revolution embedded in the three-dimensional Euclidean space of our physical environment. This saddle-shaped Beltrami surface can be generated by revolving a curve known as a "tractrix" around an axis. A tractrix is a curve such that the length of every tangent from its point of contact to its intersection with the axis is a constant. The curve is so called, because it was conceived as described by one end of a tangent line of *fixed* length as the other end is tracked along the axis, which the curve approaches asymptotically on both sides.

The Beltrami surface generated by revolving the tractrix around the axis qualifies as a model of plane hyperbolic geometry in the following special sense: Suppose two-dimensional beings confined to this surface were to seek out those curves on their surface which have the so-called "geodesic" property that the lengths of portions of these curves connecting *nearby* points are smaller than the corresponding lengths of any other connecting curves. Let these geodesic curves now be called "straights," even though they would *not*, of course, qualify as straights of the three-dimensional Euclidean embedding space. Then it turns out that this system of "straights" or "geodesics" would satisfy the postulates of plane hyperbolic geometry, notably the Hyperbolic Parallel Postulate.

In a similar manner, if we apply the name "straight line" to the great circles on the surface of a sphere embedded in three-dimensional Euclidean space, then that surface is a model of the kind of two-dimensional non-Euclidean geometry in which there are no parallels at all. For the great circles qualify as geodesics of the sphere, and all great circles on the sphere intersect. This latter species of non-Euclidean geometry is known as "spherical" or "double-elliptic" geometry. And it is clear that the failure of great circles to qualify as straights or geodesics of the three-dimensional Euclidean embedding space does *not* prevent the surface of a sphere from being a model of the kind of non-Euclidean "plane" in which there are no parallels at all.

The fact that the Beltrami surface and the surface of the sphere can respectively be models of the hyperbolic and spherical kinds of plane non-Euclidean geometry can be used to establish the following important conclusion: *if* Euclidean geometry itself is consistent, then each of these non-Euclidean geometries must likewise be logically consistent or free from internal contradictions. The basis for this conditional consistency of the non-Euclidean geometries is furnished by the following consideration. To each sentence of the language of plane hyperbolic geometry pertaining to the Beltrami surface there corresponds a sentence of three-dimensional Euclidean geometry *describing the very same facts about the physical configurations on the surface in a different language.*

Hence, if there were a logical inconsistency in the two-dimensional hyperbolic description of the Beltrami surface, there would need to be a corresponding contradition in its three-dimensional Euclidean description. For a logical inconsistency, if present, would arise *not* from the particular geometrical words that are applied to the various physical configurations on the surface, but from the formal logical relations between the sentences pertaining to these configurations. Analogous considerations establish the conditional consistency of the spherical kind of non-Euclidean geometry. The *mathematical* credentials of the non-Euclidean geometries are therefore as good as those of Euclidean geometry.

When reached at the beginning of the nineteenth century, this conclusion was of momentous significance: it rendered untenable the age-old belief that Euclidean geometry had codified the only *logically possible* geometrical relations in physical space, a belief which led to the doctrine that observational findings were therefore *not* necessary to establish the physical truth of the Euclidean system. This belief had been a major source of support both for philosophical rationalism and for the philosophy of Kant in their dispute with the empiricists. The empiricists had maintained that our knowledge of the geometrical structure of physical space requires observational justification no less than our beliefs about the medicinal properties of certain drugs, for example.

The discovery of non-Euclidean geometries by the mathematicians showed, as Lobachevski and Gauss were quick to realize, that it is an *experimental* question whether the paths in three-dimensional space which we call "straight lines" (for example, the paths of light rays) exhibit the relations specified by one of the non-Euclidean geometries *or* those formulated by Euclid's postulates. But these mathematicians were also aware that observations on an *astronomical* scale might be required to disclose the non-Euclidean character of physical space. For the mathematics of the non-Euclidean geometries shows that the discrepancy between non-Euclidean and Euclidean results becomes smaller upon diminishing the size of the region which we explore mensurationally.

If the reader will glance at the 1961 volume (No. 134) of the American journal *Science,* he will find on pages 1426 and 1434 that certain astronomical methods for determining the geometric

129

structure of physical space have led some recent investigators to conclude tentatively that it is indeed non-Euclidean in the large. But their findings as to the specific kind of non-Euclideanism are quite incompatible.

I now turn to a consideration of a problem concerning the nature of time: namely, the problem of whether time is *qualitatively* non-isotropic or isotropic. This philosophical question arises in the context of *cosmic* time and has been formulated metaphorically by asking whether there is an "arrow" of time. My aim is to show that the solution of the problem of the arrow of time turns entirely on the scientific determination of the extent to which there are *irreversible* kinds of processes in nature. Thus, it will become apparent that the philosopher who endeavors to answer qualitative questions about time must rely on the findings of the natural sciences no less than must the quantitative astronomer whose concern is with temporal durations.

In order to understand the difference between *reversible* and *irreversible* kinds of processes in its bearing on the nature of time, consider the following examples of processes which seem to be irreversible. When hot water and cold water are poured into an essentially closed container, their temperatures will equalize so as to yield lukewarm water, but, at least in our ordinary experience, lukewarm water in a closed container does *not* undergo separation into hot and cold portions of water.

Similarly, we find that while the young grow old, the aged do not regain their youthful vigor. Neither do the dead rise from their graves, nor do cigarettes reconstitute themselves from their ashes. These kinds of processes are observed to be irreversible, at at least during the segment of cosmic time constituting the current epoch in our spatial region of the world. Precisely what do we mean when we term these kinds of physical and biological processes irreversible?

We mean that either the laws of nature themselves or particular conditions (often called "boundary conditions") that happen to obtain *de facto* alongside these laws *preclude* the occurrence of the temporal inverses of these processes with increasing time. Hence the irreversibility of a kind of process is constituted by the nonexistence or impossibility of its temporal inverse. Thus, our awareness of the irreversibility of the process of chewing food or of mixing cream with coffee enables us to discern whether or not a silent film of a dinner party has been played backward to us. For if the film were to show a whole beefsteak reassembling itself from chewed pieces, we would know that it had been played backward.

Let us consider the significance of the presumed fact that there are kinds of sequences of states *ABCD*, occurring with increasing time, such that it would not also be possible to encounter the *opposite* sequence *DCBA* with increasing time. Suppose, for example, *ABCD* are successive kinds of states of a house that burns down completely with increasing time. Then there will be no case of the inverse kind of sequence *DCBA* with increasing time, since the latter would constitute the resurrection of a house from debris.

Thus, this *opposite* kind of sequence *DCBA* would exist only in the direction of decreasing time, while the first kind of sequence *ABCD* would *not* obtain in the latter direction. Accordingly, comparison of the structures of the opposite directions of time shows that, at least for the segment of cosmic time constituting the current epoch in our spatial region of the world, some kinds of sequences of states exhibited by the one direction are different from the corresponding sequences found in the other. Hence we say that, at least locally, time is non-isotropic rather than isotropic. And, in this sense, we recognize non-isotropy as one of the striking qualitative features of time. Eddington has referred to this feature by the misleading metaphor of time's arrow.

The dependence of such non-isotropy as is exhibited by time on the irreversible character of the processes obtaining in the universe can be thrown into bolder relief by noting what kind of time there would be if there were no irreversible processes at all but only reversible processes. To forestall misunderstandings of such a hypothetical eventuality, it must be pointed out at once that our very existence as human beings having *memories* would then be impossible. Hence, it would be entirely misconceived to engage in the inherently doomed attempt to imagine the posited eventuality *within the framework of our actual memory-charged experiences,* and then to be dismayed by the failure of such an attempt. We might as well try to imagine the *visual* color of radiation in the infra-red or ultra-violet parts of the spectrum.

Now, *if all* kinds of natural processes *were* in fact reversible in the sense of actually having temporal inverses, time would indeed be isotropic. To see this, consider an example of a *reversible* physical process: the frictionless rolling of a ball over a path *AD* in accord with Newton's laws, say from *A* to *D*. This motion is reversible because there is a return motion over the same path, but from *D* to *A*, which is the temporal inverse of the motion from *A* to *D* and is likewise allowed by Newton's laws. Thus, for every position of the ball allowed by Newton's laws at a time $+t$, these laws allow precisely the same position at the corresponding time $-t$. In the case of reversible processes, therefore, the sequences of positions along the *opposite* directions of the time axis are, as it were, temporal *mirror images* of each other. Hence, if all of the processes of nature were reversible, time would be *isotropic.*

It is now apparent that the nature of time is *not* something which is apart from the particular kinds of processes obtaining in the universe. Instead, the nature of time is rooted in the very character of these processes. And in the context of the irreversible processes existing in our physical environment, the *earlier* of two non-equilibrium states of a mixture of hot and cold water, for example, is the state in which the temperatures are less equalized.

Einstein inquired what it is about two non-coinciding events that makes for the existence of a *temporal* relation between them. And he concluded that such a temporal relation derives from some *physical* relation sustained by such events instead of obtaining *per se.* Thus he was driven to articulate the physical foundations of the temporal relations "earlier than," "later than," and "simultaneous with."

To someone imbued with Newtonian assumptions about the behavior of transported clocks, it suggests itself that the physical basis for the obtaining of the relation of simultaneity among spatially separated events is the following: two clocks U_1 and U_2

are transported to *separate* places from a common point in space at which they had identical readings, and then event E occurs at the location of clock U_1, and event E' at the pace of clock U_2 such that the readings of U_1 and U_2 are the same. But the belief that this criterion of simultaneity will yield *consistent* answers when different clocks assume the role of either U_1 or U_2 presupposes the following Newtonian assumption as to the behavior of transported clocks: if two clocks U_1 and U_2 are initially synchronized at the *same* place A and then transported via paths of *different lengths* to a different place B such that their arrivals at B coincide, then U_1 and U_2 will still be synchronized at B. And if U_1 and U_2 were brought to B via the *same* path (or via different paths of *equal* length) such that their arrivals do *not* coincide, then their initial synchronization would likewise be preserved. But Einstein thought that by the beginning of the twentieth century there were good grounds for denying precisely this Newtonian assumption. Specifically, he postulated that the initial synchronization of the two clocks would be destroyed under the aforementioned conditions of transport upon their arrival at point B.

If Einstein's postulate of the destruction of synchronism by transport is granted, however, then it follows at once that a given pair of events at points A and B would or would *not* be simultaneous depending upon which particular one of the *discordant* clocks at B would serve as the time standard at B. But this dependence of simultaneity on the particular transported clock that is used presents us with the following important result: identical numerical readings exhibited by two initially synchronized clocks after they are transported to *separate* places *cannot* constitute the physical basis for a relation of simultaneity between events at these separate places which is independent of which particular clock is used.

Since clock transport won't do, Einstein assumed that the various objective relations of temporal order between spatially separated events depend on the obtaining or non-obtaining between them of a physical relation of connectibility by a causal influence chain. And this raised the question as to the particular conditions under which a pair of spatially separated events can be simultaneous. Two events which *are* connectible by an influ-ence chain will be temporally separated rather than simultane-ous. Hence a *necessary* condition for the simultaneity of two spatially separated events is that they *not* be connectible by any causal influence chain. Is this condition also sufficient to guar-antee the obtaining of a relation of simultaneity which is unique in the sense that one and only one event at a point P will be simultaneous with a given event occurring at a point Q else-where in space?

The answer to this question of uniqueness depends entirely on whether there is at the point P just one or more than one event which cannot be connected with the given event at Q by a causal influence. And Einstein introduced a fundamental inno-vation into physics here by postulating that, rather than merely one event, there is always a whole interval of events at P which are not causally connectible with the event at Q. We shall now show that this innovation is a direct consequence of the follow-ing novel assumption to which Einstein was led by a thought experiment undertaken at the age of sixteen: light or electro-magnetic waves *in vacuo* are the fastest possible influence chains in nature.

To see clearly the bearing of this postulate concerning light *in vacuo* on the uniqueness question before us, I ask the reader to take pencil and paper and to consider a light ray which leaves the point P at a time t_1 on the clock at P so as to arrive at the point Q upon the occurrence there of a given event E_2. Let this light ray be instantaneously reflected at Q so as to return to P at a time t_3. Furthermore, let the events constituting the departure of the light ray from P and its return to P be called, respectively, E_1 and E_3. We recall that the times of these events on the clock at P are t_1 and t_3, respectively. Now, if light is the fastest causal chain of nature *in vacuo*, then *none* of the infinitude of events occurring at the point P during the time interval there between t_1 and t_3 can be connected with the given event E_2 at Q by a physically pos-sible causal influence. For every such influence originating at one of these events would fail to reach the point Q early enough to coincide there with E_2, and no causal chain emitted at Q upon E_2's occurrence could reach P prior to the occurrence of E_3.

But if all members of the infinite set of events at P comprising the interval between t_1 and t_3 are on a par in regard to their not being causally connectible with E_2, then there is no objective physical basis for claiming that any one of them is uniquely simultaneous with E_2, as there would be in a universe conforming to Newtonian assumptions.

It is, therefore, only by convention or definition that some one of these events comes to be simultaneous with E_2. Unlike the Newtonian situation, in which there was only a single event E which could be significantly held to be simultaneous with E_2, the physical facts postulated by Einstein's theory of relativity require the introduction, within every inertial frame S, of a convention stipulating which particular pair of causally non-connectible events will be called "simultaneous" in system S. This conventionality of simultaneity within every inertial system makes for the fact that the simultaneity criterion of the system requires the choice of a particular numerical value t_2 between t_1 and t_3 as the temporal name to be assigned to E_2. If we choose a value of t_2 which is *halfway* between t_1 and t_3, then the one-way transit velocities of light along PQ and QP become equal. But if we choose a different value of t_2 between t_1 and t_3 for setting the clock at Q upon the occurrence of E_2 there, then these one-way velocities of light in opposite directions become unequal. In section 1 of his fundamental paper on the special theory of relativity, Einstein put this point by writing: "We establish *by definition* that the 'time' required by light to travel from A to B equals the 'time' it requires to travel from B to A."

In the mathematical formulation of the special theory of relativity Einstein does choose a criterion of simultaneity within *each* inertial system so as to render the one-way velocities of light in opposite directions equal. But this then has the consequence that relatively moving inertial systems will each choose a *different* event within the interval between E_1 and E_3 at P to be simultaneous with E_2 at Q, if their relative motion is always the line PQ.

13 PROBLEMS OF MICROPHYSICS

Paul Feyerabend

It is frequently assumed that the development of physics consists of long periods of success which are interrupted by short periods of crisis. Successful periods are dominated either by a single theory or by a few theories which complement each other. These theories are used for the explanation of known observational facts and for the prediction of new facts. Attempts to explain a particular fact may be difficult and require great ingenuity. Still, there will be little doubt that the theory is correct, and that the difficulty will one day be overcome. Difficulties, therefore, are not regarded as being of any fundamental importance. Professor T. Kuhn, who in his recent book *The Structure of Scientific Revolutions* has investigated the matter in some detail, expresses this attitude by calling them "puzzles," not "problems." A puzzle may need great mental effort in order to be solved; however, it does *not* necessitate the revision of basic theory.

Periods of crisis have a very different character. The optimism characterizing the successful periods has gone; problems have turned up which seem to indicate that a drastic change is needed. Numerous suggestions are made, many different theories are proposed, investigated, abandoned. Whereas the most conspicuous characteristic of a successful period of scientific research—or of a *normal* period, as it has been called more recently—is the fact that a *single point of view* is used, and strictly adhered to, a crisis leads to the emergence of a great many theories. Normal science is *monistic;* crises are *pluralistic.*

This *factual* account of the history of the sciences is almost always supplemented, at least implicitly, by an *evaluation.* Ac-

136

cording to this evaluation, normal science is desirable and crises, or revolutions, are undesirable. Of course, a crisis leads to the discovery of fundamental weaknesses in the accepted theories, and it therefore precipitates progress to new and better theories. But first, it is regarded only as a *stage* in a process leading to improvement and normal science. The latter is still the *aim*. And second, it is often added that a crisis would not have occurred had the previous theories been formulated with due circumspection. In short, it is believed that science is essentially normal science. Crises are embarrassments, periods of confusion which should be passed through as quickly as possible and which should not be unduly extended.

The general aversion toward periods of crisis has a marked influence upon what one could call the "ethics" of a scientific community; it also influences the appointed court historians of this community—the historians of science. Let me deal with the latter first. Historians of science are usually intent on stretching any successful period of normal scientific activity until it almost covers the whole of the history of science from the so-called scientific revolution of the sixteenth and seventeenth centuries until about 1900. To present the revolution of the sixteenth and seventeenth centuries as a crisis is regarded as quite legitimate: this, after all, was the emergence of science from myth and metaphysics. Nor is it possible to overlook the fundamental character of the more recent changes brought about by the discovery of the quantum of action. But the period in between these two dates is usually represented as a period of continued success, as a period where more and more *known* facts are subject to treatment by the received theories, and where more and more *new* facts are discovered.

The effect of the predilection for a theoretical monism upon the community of scientists is perhaps even more pronounced. Any procedure which *decreases* the impact of existing difficulties is welcome. Any procedure which *increases* this impact and which suggests that the difficulty completely undermines the received opinion is frowned upon. Radical methods are used against those engaging in such subversive activity. It is of course no longer possible to eliminate opponents by recourse to *violence*. However, they are still silenced most effectively by the refusal to publish their work, or by the refusal to take such work seriously.

Some of the most extraordinary thinkers had to suffer from this unwillingness of the scientific community to change the delicate balance between difficulties and successes which characterizes a normal period. Of course, this conservatism is not the whole story. There exists hardly another domain of knowledge that is as full of daring innovations and of unusual ideas as is science. Yet the conservatism must not be overlooked, since it will influence the *official* doctrine and will thereby contribute to the manner in which existing difficulties are evaluated. This has an immediate application to our topic—the problems of contemporary microphysical theory.

The history of the quantum theory is one of the most interesting and least explored periods in the history of science. It is a marvelous example of the way in which philosophical speculation, empirical research, and mathematical ingenuity can jointly contribute to the development of physical theory. In order properly to understand its interpretation, we must give a short account of the history of science from about 1600 to the present. Of course, this account will have to be very superficial. Yet I hope that it will give some insight into principles which today are regarded as fundamental elements of the scientific method.

We must distinguish three periods. The *first period* is dominated by the Aristotelian philosophy. This philosophy contained a highly sophisticated physics which in turn was based upon a somewhat radical empiricism. The Aristotelians at the time of Galileo are still being described by many historians as emptyheaded dogmatists and the real force of their arguments against the motion of the earth as well as the difficulties which these arguments created for the heliocentric system are seldom properly appreciated.

The *second period* is the classical physics of Galileo, Newton, Faraday, Maxwell. This is one of the most curious periods in the history of knowledge. The official philosophy is still empiricism—and indeed a very militant empiricism it is. Speculation is discouraged; hypotheses are frowned upon; experimentation and derivation from observational results are regarded as the only legitimate manner of obtaining knowledge. The domain of factual knowledge is considerably extended. The theories based upon this new material belong to the most subtle inventions of the human mind. At the same time, they seem to fit perfectly the empiricist ideal: most of them seemed to have been obtained by a strict mathematical derivation from experience. We know now, mainly through the work of Duhem and Einstein, that none of these alleged derivations is valid; that the defended theories go *beyond* existing observational results and that they are also *inconsistent* with them.

We therefore witness here the astonishing spectacle of men who invent bold new theories; who believe that these theories are nothing but a reflection of observable facts; who support this belief by a procedure which is apparently a deduction from observations; who in this way deceive both themselves and their contemporaries and make them think that the empirical philosophy has been strictly adhered to. We have here a period of *schizophrenia* characterized by a complete break between philosophical theory and scientific practice. This is an age when the scientist does one thing and insists that he is doing, and must do, another.

To be sure, a few people were aware of the difference between the philosophical ideal and the actual practice, for example, the philosophers Berkeley and Hume and the physicists Faraday and Boltzmann. But the success of classical physics was taken to expose their argument as an exhibition of typical philosophical sophistry. This period of schizophrenia is terminated by the crisis connected with the invention of the theory of relativity and the discovery of the quantum of action.

It is hardly possible to overestimate the shock created by these changes. For almost two hundred and fifty years one had believed that one was in possession of the correct method; that one had applied it properly; and that one had in this way obtained valuable and trustworthy knowledge. It was of course necessary, now and then, to revise a theory or a point of view, but such events were regarded as being of minor importance or were perhaps even completely neglected. It now turned out that one had been basing one's inquiry on the wrong foundations. It is interesting to see how scientists reacted to this discovery.

Einstein drew the correct conclusion: science is incompatible with the empirical method, at least as envisaged by many classical physicists. A scientist intuitively invents theories which always go far beyond experience and which are therefore vulnerable to future considerations. The breakdown of a theory, or of a general point of view, is not an indication of faulty method; its possibility is essential to science. Einstein also quite explicitly broke with the tradition of presenting a new theory as the result of a deduction from facts. His first paper on relativity, "Zur Elektrodynamik bewegter Körper," does not start with the enunciations of facts, but of *principles* such as the principle of the constancy of the velocity of light in all inertial systems. Nor is it related to experimental facts in any simple and straightforward manner (the basic ideas it contains were developed before Einstein had heard of the Michelson-Morley experiment). The development leading to the quantum theory was based on a very different philosophy.

To start with, there was a period of experimentation when hardly any fundamental law remained unchallenged. "Every student of physics was trained in the art of overthrowing basic laws," writes the philosopher Hugo Dingler about this period (which Dingler himself regarded with a very critical eye). The investigations carried out during this period, mainly under the guidance of Bohr, led to a curious result: there existed classical laws which *remained strictly valid* in the microphysical domain. This suggested that classical physics, though surely not adequate, was still not *completely* incorrect. It seemed to contain a factual core which had to be freed from non-factual trappings. This suspicion was reinforced by the inclination of most physicists to retain classical empiricism as the correct scientific method.

The breakdown of classical physics now proved to them that this empiricism had not been properly applied. Or, to put it in different words, it proved to them that classical physics was physics only in part. It contained metaphysical constituents. Combining this *philosophical* conviction with the *factual* discovery of classical laws which were still strictly valid, they now set out: (1) to give an account of all the valuable parts of classical physics; (2) to add to this account the features dependent on the quantum of action; and (3) to find a coherent formal apparatus for the presentation of both (1) and (2). The principle of correspondence was used in order to discover the parts of this formalism; later on it was replaced by the method of quantization which transforms its more intuitive content into a mechanical procedure.

It is most important to realize that a theory obtained in the fashion just indicated is very different from universal theories such as Einstein's theory of relativity. The concepts of Einstein's theory can be applied to the world without qualification. They are relational concepts, true, but the relations asserted to hold are objective and independent of the specific experimental arrangement used for ascertaining their presence.

The theory of relativity is therefore accessible to a *realistic interpretation* which turns it into a description of the objective (relational) features of the world we live in—a description that is correct whether or not experiments are actually carried out. The new quantum theory that was envisaged by Bohr and by his followers could not be a theory of this kind. For though its descriptive concepts are still those of classical physics, they have been stripped of what might be regarded as their metaphysical trappings. Thus, originally a concept such as the concept of position was considered universally applicable—classical particles always have *some* well-defined position.

Now, the conceptual spring cleaning connected with the attempt to uncover the empirical core of classical physics and to utilize it for the purpose of prediction and explanation eliminates the possibility of universal application. We may use the concept of position, and the corresponding more general concept of a particle, only if certain experimental requirements are first satisfied. Many descriptive concepts are restricted in an analogous manner. The theory therefore can no longer be regarded as an account of a microlevel as it exists independently of observation and experiment; it can only say what will happen if certain experimental conditions are first satisfied. It is incapable of giving an account of what happens in between experiments. It is therefore *nothing but* a predictive device. Bohr's principle of complementarity gives a very striking intuitive account of the manner in which this predictive device works and thereby provides at least a partial picture of the microworld.

The interpretation which we have just sketched was then used to make some important predictions concerning the future development of the quantum theory. The basic structure of the quantum theory, the use of formalisms with non-commuting variables acting on a Hilbert-space or a suitable extension of it, and the corresponding intuitive feature of complementary aspects in the world are the result of an analysis that has bared the observational core of classical physics. This structure and these features are at last firmly based upon experience, and they are therefore final and irrevocable. We are here not presented ". . . with a point of view which we may adopt, or reject, according to whether it agrees, or does not agree, with some philosophical criterion. It is the unique result of an adaptation of our ideas to a new experimental situation," writes A. N. Rosenfeld of Copenhagen.

It is of course admitted that the quantum theory will have to undergo some decisive changes in order to be able to cope with new phenomena and that physicists will be requested to introduce new concepts for the description of new facts. It is also occasionally considered legitimate to try different approaches and to develop different formalisms such as G. F. Chew's S-matrix theory for strong interactions, Heisenberg's unified field theories, and others. Nevertheless, it will be pointed out that however large these changes, and however different these formalisms, they will leave unchanged the basic elements just mentioned, which are in any case needed to give them empirical content. The future development, therefore, can only be in the direction of greater indeterminism, and still further away from the point of view of classical physics. This attitude influences in an important way the evaluation of the existing theoretical problems of microphysics.

It is clear that such problems will now appear to be minor technical "puzzles" which do not necessitate a revision of the basic structure of the quantum theory. It may be granted that new mathematical techniques will be needed for the purpose of bringing about a closer agreement between theory and experiment; yet it will be emphasized that these new techniques are still in need of interpretation, and that the interpretation must be carried out in the customary manner, by reference to the idea of complementarity. It is also admitted that some of the notions which had to be introduced in order to account for features going *beyond* complementarity may be faulty, and need qualification. (Non-conservation of parity in cases of weak interaction is a case in point.)

Still, such modifications will not affect the indeterministic framework. We have here, therefore, the beginning of a new period of *normal* science. The signs characteristic of a normal period such as aversion to a different approach in fundamental matters are already present. Such aversion is directed not only against the ideas of D. Bohm and J. P. Vigier, which to the careless observer may indeed look like a step back, but it has also condemned the novel ideas of A. P. Feynman and F. J. Dyson and it is also responsible for the initial rejection of E. C. G. Stückelberg's marvelous work. Only straight field theory, which seems best to fit the point of view of complementarity, is permitted. It is also believed that this normal period may be expected to last forever. Previous crises were due to the existence of metaphysical ingredients in the basis of science. These ingredients have been removed. Further development will therefore consist in the gradual addition of new facts and the gradual erection of a tower of facts on a solid basis. Minor crises may still occur, but they will modify only the upper layers of the tower. They will not necessitate the recasting of the fundaments on which the tower rests.

Now it should be obvious that the *reasons* given for such a prophecy are not acceptable. One of the main reasons given is that the indeterministic framework and the idea of complementarity and its corollaries are an immediate expression of experimental fact. This does not put them into a uniquely privileged position. Experimental results only show that suggested laws which are in accord with them are approximately valid. Given a set of experimental results, it is therefore always possible to devise alternative sets of experimental laws which agree with them within the margin of error characteristic for the equipment used.

The set of basic experimental laws, defended by the orthodox, is therefore only one among many possible sets. Another argument given in defense of the point of view of the orthodox, which is now often identified with the point of view of field theory, is that we need the descriptive terms of classical physics in order to express experimental results, and for this reason that alternative accounts are bound to fail. They might succeed in producing a *formalism*. However, in the attempt to give empirical meaning to this formalism the classical terms will again have to be used, and with them the point of view of complementarity.

As regards this argument, it must be noted that a new point of view will of course also have to provide new terms for the description of the observational level. It is quite unreasonable to assume that observational terms possess greater stability than do theoretical terms. Observational terms usually are the terms of some theory, and since they have been applied under the most common circumstances, they have become *familiar*. However, familiarity is no guarantee of adequacy—quite the contrary. For example, certain observational terms used in the Aristotelian physics were found to be inadequate and in need of replacement. The transition to the classical physics of Galileo and Newton would have been quite impossible without such replacement.

It *is* therefore possible to abandon a given observational terminology and to replace it by a different terminology. This, by the way, shows the absurdity in the argument of some contemporary physicists, notably Heisenberg and G. F. von Weizsäcker, which maintains that since physicists are endowed with a classical observational vocabulary they will forever be unable to look at observable matters in a different manner. It is clear that an application of this principle at the time of Galileo would have given great comfort to the Aristotelians.

To repeat: It *is* possible to abandon a certain observational terminology and to replace it by a different terminology. But *should* we do such a thing? Clearly the decision will depend on whether we have convinced ourselves that the terminology in use is inadequate. Only very *fundamental* difficulties could have sufficient persuasive power. It is therefore necessary for us to find out whether the present quantum theory is indeed faced with fundamental difficulties.

It is clear that the distinction between periods of crisis and normal periods does not help us to answer this question. This distinction describes the situation *from the outside,* as it were, and *after* scientists have made up their minds. The individual scientists whose individual decision will contribute to the phenomenon which Professor Kuhn has described so clearly cannot base his decision on what is a *result* of the decisions made. At this point, Professor Kuhn's book seems to suggest—in accordance with what is thought to be the case by many thinkers, physicists and philosophers alike, though perhaps not in accordance with the intentions of the author—that the *historical situation* might provide a valuable guide, a guide, moreover, whose advice *should not be neglected.*

It suggests that a period of crisis *announces itself* by an accumulation of unsolved problems and by a feeling of general uneasiness and frustration, and that a separate analysis of the total theoretical situation by the individual scientist is not needed. This, it seems to me, means putting the cart before the horse. A mere accumulation of "puzzles" is neither necessary nor sufficient to create *genuine* problems and to suggest that what is needed is a basic revision, not a minor adjustment. At the beginning, Newton's astronomy was faced with an ever-increasing number of difficulties, but very few people saw in this an indication that Newton's theory was incorrect. The past triumphs of the theory, the new vision provided by it, the astonishing initial successes, inspired sufficient confidence.

The theory of relativity, on the other hand, was not preceded by an *accumulation* of difficulties. Most of the problems which can now be cited in favor of its invention had already been solved by H. A. Lorentz's theory of the electron. What Einstein sought was a general principle, comparable to the second law of thermodynamics, that could be relied on in the changes which seemed to surround the discovery of the quantum of action. He obtained this principle from fairly simple theoretical considera-

145

tions, involving the symmetry properties of classical mechanics and electrodynamics, not under the pressure of adverse empirical material.

The further development leads to the general theory of relativity. It is this new point of view which raises certain annoying "puzzles," such as the excess movement of the perihelion of Mercury, to genuine problems, and thereby precipitates progress. And *it could not be otherwise*. After all, an accumulation of puzzles will cease to be regarded as a challenge to calculation on the basis of the old theory and will assume the appearance of a genuine new problem only if it is seen on the background of a new point of view that imposes upon it a coherence different from the coherence postulated by the established doctrine.

The recognition of a problem as fundamental therefore depends on the development, *in addition to the received theory,* of a new point of view. This new point of view may of course be refuted by future research, but without it there is no chance of fundamental progress. Nor will it be possible to develop new points of view at once in a very detailed fashion; a vague metaphysical idea will in most cases be the starting point. The fruitfulness of new points of view is confirmed, apart from these more abstract considerations, by many episodes in the history of the sciences, and especially by the history of the atomic theory itself.

The exclusiveness of normal science, the strong moralizing against the use of new points of view which deviate from the established modes of thinking, is therefore self-defeating. If successful, it will prevent the physicists from discovering the weaknesses of their favorite theory. It is also a little naïve to suppose, as P. A. M. Dirac did in a recent talk, that the more general, or "philosophical," difficulties of a theory are of no importance for a physicist and that the progress of physical theory will automatically dissolve them. The situation is just the other way around.

Philosophical difficulties emerge from the comparison of a physical theory to a more general point of view that has not yet been developed in detail and that is not in agreement with the basic principles of the theory. As we have pointed out, such comparison is the motor which propels science, and the solution of the difficulties created by it is necessary if we want to achieve not only a few minor adaptations but also fundamental progress. It is important to repeat that the standard ideology of normal science, viewed in the light of these considerations, turns out to be a hindrance to such progress. Theoretical pluralism should be encouraged, not frowned upon. It is only such pluralism, and not the accumulation of "puzzles," which advances knowledge and which prevents it from becoming the perfectly embalmed corpse of what at some time was an exciting discovery.

The consequence is, of course, that, unlike politics, in science the battle cry should be: *Revolution in permanence!*

14 ASPECTS OF EXPLANATION IN BIOLOGICAL THEORY

Morton Beckner

In a much discussed paper, published in 1948, Carl Hempel and Paul Oppenheim described a pattern of explanation that has since become known as the "deductive model." In outline, its major theses are the following: If we call a statement of the event or phenomenon to be explained the explanandum, and a statement of the information offered to account for it the explanans, then, in a sound explanation the following conditions must be met: the explanans is true and contains at least one general law; and the explanandum is entailed by (or is deducible from) the explanans.

The deductive model makes an immediate appeal to students of the logic of the sciences. It is in a sense a formulation of a number of philosophical ideas that are at least as old as Aristotle: namely, that explanations are special cases of deductive arguments, and that some of the premises of these arguments are universal truths. Accordingly, this account does justice to the common-sense notion that we have explained a phenomenon only when we have cited sufficient conditions for its occurrence— that is, when we have shown that, things being the way they are, the phenomenon could not fail to occur. Hempel and Oppenheim unhesitatingly draw the corollary that we have explained a phenomenon only if we would have been in a position to predict it by citing its sufficient conditions.

Subsequent discussions of the logic of explanation commonly employ the deductive model as a starting point. Two main types of question have been raised about it: first, do the existing de-

scriptions of the model in fact explicate the patterns of explanation it is aimed at formulating; and second, what is the scope of
the model? A number of critics have argued that the model has
internal difficulties, and also that there are some patterns of explanation that the model does not explicate at all. In particular
it has been argued that the model's natural habitat is the
physical sciences, and that it founders in biology, psychology, and
the social sciences.

The general thesis of this essay is that a revised form of the
deductive model is indeed applicable to *all* explanations.

In particular, explanation in the biological sciences is widely
regarded as offering especially intractable cases for the deductive
model—historical and teleological explanations, for instance. I
shall not have time to apply the revision of the model to these
cases in detail, but I shall by the choice of examples show by
indirection how it might be done.

The revision I shall offer is perhaps extensive enough to warrant a change in terminology. I shall call it the "implicational
model of explanation." The respects in which it differs from the
deductive model are explicitly designed to take into account four
features of explanation, and especially of explanation in biology,
that the deductive model, as it now stands, does not formulate.

The first is this: An ostensible explanation "*P*, therefore *E*,"
according to the deductive model, is essentially defective unless *P*
entails *E*. If *P* does not entail *E*, the explanation is regarded as
unsound, elliptical, or, at the very least, a sketch of an explanation, to be filled out by subsequent research. The *only* semantical
justification for this decision that I can see consists in the correct
observation that the explanation lays down a sufficient condition.
But *P*'s entailment of *E* is not the only logical relation that will
ensure that *P* is sufficient for *E*; it is enough for *P* to *imply E*.
Moreover, from the point of view of common usage, there seem
to be all sorts of explanations which are perfectly complete, but
which miss on the requirement of deducibility. Accordingly, in
the implicational model, the requirement that *P* entail *E* is replaced by the requirement that *P* imply *E*. It will soon be clear
that this change in some ways makes no difference at all, but in
other ways makes a great deal of difference.

Second: The deductive model does full justice to the requirement that the explanans lay down a sufficient condition for the explanandum. But it does not take into account a simple semantical point, namely, that we should not regard a phenomenon as explained unless we had cited (or at least presupposed) some condition whose absence would lead to the non-occurrence of the phenomenon. For example, suppose there is a country X in which there is no smallpox, and which has undertaken an exhaustive immunization program. Suppose further that the laws of immunology are so strong that we can deduce the absence of smallpox from these laws, together with the information about the immunization of the population.

Here we have, then, a paradigm of explanation according to the deductive model: we have explained the absence of smallpox by reference to general laws and an immunization program. But it is clear that we should not regard the explanation as sound unless there would have been smallpox had the program not been undertaken. There may never have been an infecting organism with the boundaries of country X, or the population might not be susceptible, and so on. If any one of these conditions were realized, we should say that the absence of smallpox was due to it, and not to the immunization program, even though the immunization program is a sufficient condition for the absence of the disease. Accordingly, in the implicational model we require that the explanans either explicitly cite or, in a sense to be explained, presuppose a *necessary* as well as a sufficient condition of the explanandum.

Third: Many explanations, and especially some of those in the biological sciences, are context-dependent. I may illustrate what this means by giving a simple example of a context-dependent argument that is not an explanation. Suppose someone argues: "This animal has eight legs; therefore it is not an insect." We raise the question: Is the argument sound? Grant that the premise is true. It is clear that we can deduce the conclusion from the premise together with the statement that all insects are six-legged. But, of course, the statement that all insects are six-legged is not strictly true; all insects are six-legged except for some rare and aberrant types.

I propose to describe such arguments in the following way. It being granted that the premise *P* is true, the argument is sound if the conclusion *E* is implied by *P*. And I shall say that *P* does imply *E* in the example just cited if the insect in question is not one of the rare or aberrant types. In other words, the question whether or not an implication holds (or whether the statement "If *P*, then *E*" is true) depends upon some other fact about the context in which the implication is asserted. I shall examine in a moment the concept of implication that we need in order to make sense out of the notion of a context-dependent implication; for the present, let us simply note that the following expanded version of our example is formally valid:

P_1: This animal has eight legs.
P_2: All insects are six-legged except those of a few aberrant types.
P_3: This animal is not a member of the aberrant types.
E: Therefore, this animal is not an insect.

The implication from P_1 to E holds if P_2 and P_3 are true. The context-dependence of the implication rests on the context-dependence of P_3, the particular statement that the specimen is not an exception to a general rule. The proviso that is a part of P_2 so hedges the general rule that it is exempted from refutation by the discovery of unusual cases. Michael Scriven (see Chapter 16) has emphasized the large role such statements play in the sciences; I agree on their importance, but, unlike Scriven, I don't think their use in explanations makes all versions of the deductive model untenable. I shall call them "hedged" statements, and I shall call such statements as P_3, which disarm the hedging clause, "bypassing" statements.

We may now say that the explanation in our smallpox example is in fact a context-dependent explanation. It is sound only if it is applied to a country in which there would be smallpox in the absence of an immunization program. The explanation itself can be expanded to include a statement with the hedging clause "except regions where there are no infecting organisms, and so on," and a bypassing clause to the effect that country *X* is not one of these exceptional regions.

Four: We come now to the final feature of explanation which the deductive model misses and which the implicational model must catch. This concerns the so-called asymmetry of explanation and prediction. According to the deductive model, we have not explained a phenomenon unless we would have been in a position to predict it on the same basis. The defenders of the deductive model are not disturbed by the empirical fact that this requirement reduces to pulp the whole fabric of some sciences, including ecology, animal geography, evolution theory, ethology, developmental physiology, and many others. After all, they say, the sciences must have *some* standards. It seems, then, that the requirement is, to say the very least, whimsical; accordingly, I shall admit non-predictive explanations.

Consider another simple case: an animal geographer remarks that there are finches on the Galápagos Archipelago because some breeding specimens in the past flew over from the mainland of South America. Two points seem clear: first, that this might well be a sound and complete explanation; and second, that if their arrival in the dim past had been greeted by a local birdwatcher, he could not possibly have predicted the presence of finches in the twentieth century. This would be so even if he had access to a complete list of the laws of ecology, for this list could not rule out contingencies such as lightning, boys with air guns, and so on.

It is clear that a model which takes account of these four features of explanation will rely heavily on a suitable analysis of the logic of implication. For reasons that I cannot now specify in detail it turns out that the logic of the standard systems of material implication fails to do the job. In revising the deductive model it is also necessary to revise these systems a little. Fundamentally, we need a relation of implication that has two semantical features: First, it is possible to establish any true statement "P implies E" without presupposing or establishing the truth value of P or E. This is reasonable, since, on the face of the matter, the question whether P implies E is a question of the connections between them, not a question of their truth or falsehood. Second, if it is true that P implies E, it ought to be the case that P is relevant to E. But in the system of material implication both these requirements are of course violated; this follows from the fact that the system permits the paradoxes of strict and material implication.

Is it possible to construct a logical system (call it S) which is like a classical system of material implication except that the paradoxes are not provable? Every logician will immediately recognize that since the paradoxes are so deeply imbedded in the rules of the classical systems, S must have some rather peculiar features. A number of systems have been proposed in which the paradoxes are not provable, but all of these have been characterized by rather extensive plastic surgery on the rules of the classical systems. Rules may be deleted or restricted in various ways, but the price of eliminating the paradoxes has turned out to be the introduction of other undesirable oddities. However, there is one procedure for constructing system S that avoids these oddities: namely, the elimination of the paradoxes of implication, not by reformulating the axioms or rules of inference, but by so specifying the formation rules of S that the paradoxes turn out to be ill formed. Such a system S has been constructed, and it turns out that the formal theory of implication that it yields is very convenient for formulating a definition of implication which has the two features mentioned above and which accordingly yields just the concept needed for the formulation of the implicational model of explanation.

This concept of implication may be defined as follows: We can state two *sufficient* conditions for saying that P implies E, with the help of the formal system S. First, P implies E whenever the formal translation of "If P, then E" is a theorem in S. In other words, we shall say that P implies E if, as the deductive model requires, P entails E, the criterion of entailment being theoremhood in system S. Thus, entailment is a special case of implication: namely, an implication that can be established by purely logical procedures. In parallel fashion, explanations in which the explanans entails the explanandum will also be regarded as special cases of explanation.

The second sufficient condition of implication is the following: P implies E whenever there is some true statement G which, being given, provides the grounds for the establishment in S of

"If *P*, then *E*" by purely logical procedures. Or stated more formally: *P* implies *E* whenever there is some true *G* such that the compound statement "If *G*, then: if *P*, then *E*" is a theorem in *S*.

In summary: Implication is regarded as either outright entailment or as enthymematic entailment, the unstated premise of the enthymeme being some true statement. The rules of system *S* are the rules for assessing the formal validity of ostensible entailments.

Let us call the true statement *G* in the above schema the "ground" of the implication from *P* to *E*. The formal apparatus of the logical system *S* ensures that the ground of any implication must be formally relevant to *P* and *E*; and it further ensures that the implication is independent of the truth values of *P* and *E*, except that the implication cannot be true when *P* is true and *E* false. The question of whether or not an implication which is not an entailment holds is thus to be settled by the *joint* application of two procedures: first, the logical procedure of determining whether or not a statement is a theorem of *S*; and second, the extralogical procedure of determining whether or not the ground is true.

Questions regarding the logical features of special types of explanation, such as historical, teleological, or motivational, may now be construed in a simple manner: they are questions concerning the status and internal logical form of the grounds of possible implications.

We have now before us the pieces of a jigsaw puzzle, and it only remains to put them together and contemplate the whole. The whole we are after is a comprehensive picture of the logical pattern of all types of explanation; the pieces of the puzzle are the following: an explanation must in some sense lay down a necessary and a sufficient condition of the explanandum *E*, which need not be the *same* condition; the explanans *P* must imply *E*, and may or may not entail *E*; it is possible for an explanation to be context-dependent; it is possible to explain *E* even though the prediction of *E* would have been impossible in principle; *P* must have a certain generality, at least enough to ensure that *P* and *E* are not simply equivalent; and, finally, we have a formal system S of implication which avoids the paradoxes of implication and which permits an implication to be context-dependent.

We may assemble the puzzle by specifying the general pattern of explanation and treating various explanations as special cases of the pattern.

I suggest that a proposed explanation "P, therefore E" is to be regarded as sound only if the following conditions are realized.

1. P is true.
2. P can be analyzed into two conjuncts, P_1 and P_2, and there exist true statements G_1 and G_2 such that the total statement, "If G_1, G_2, and P_1, then P_2 implies and is implied by E," is a theorem in S. There may be any combination of null G_1's, G_2's, and P_1's, except that not all three can be null.

I shall call G_1 the "sufficiency ground," G_2 the "necessity ground," and P_1 the "generality parameter" of the explanation "P, therefore E." This pattern has the following properties. Its simplest form is "If G, then P implies and is implied by E." The only simpler case would be "P implies and is implied by E"; but this would merely be a pattern for *ad hoc* verbiage, so we rule it out. In general G_1, the sufficiency ground, is simply the ground, in the sense first described, of the main implication; its presence allows us to relax the requirement that P entail E.

Most explanations in the sciences do not explicitly lay down a necessary condition for E; but, as I have argued, P does not explain E unless P is necessary for E or unless P makes some reference to a necessary condition. Hence the introduction into the pattern of the necessity ground G_2. If G_2 is null, then P is of course already explicitly necessary for E. The division of P into P_1 and P_2 is required in many explanations by the fact that P is already rather more general than E, so it could not be the case that E implies the whole of P.

The context-dependence of the explanation as a whole is due to the fact that either or both implications in the biconditional "P_2 implies and is implied by E" may be context-dependent. Moreover, the grounds G_1 and G_2 may both contain hedging and bypassing clauses, and of course the assessment of a bypassing clause requires careful and informed judgment concerning the subject matter in question. This means that the truth of the implications in the biconditional depended upon features of the subject matter not explicitly mentioned in the explanation.

The possibility of using hedged grounds for an implication makes clear why, and in what sense, we are prepared to admit non-predictive explanations. The typical hedging clause admits exceptions to a rule but does not specify closely what sort of exceptions; hence the need for informed and intelligent judgment. And although, for instance, we could not possibly specify all the factors that might wipe the finches off the Galápagos, and therefore we could not formulate the general law describing the conditions under which finches propagate, their *post facto* presence is very strong evidence in favor of the bypassing clause.

In other words, the implicational model admits non-predictive explanations in the following sense: An explanation "*P*, therefore *E*" is sound only if *P* in fact implies *E*; whether or not *P* implies *E* may depend upon facts about the subject matter that neither *P* nor *E* mentions. This is, in general, true for all implications that are not entailments. As a special case, the implication may depend upon (or, in technical language, may be grounded on) contingencies that are not yet realized in the time interval occupied by the phenomena cited in the explanans. In short, I am so using the term "implication" that it makes sense to say that the truth of the statement "*P* implies *E*" could not in some cases be established by reference to available information.

A final word about the effect of construing explanation in the way I suggest. The implicational model is certainly more tolerant than the deductive model. Indeed, I think some philosophers would say that the admission of hedged statements into explanations is simply to give up all hope of using a logic of explanation as a critical standard. In answer to this it should be noted that almost all the generalities we ordinarily employ in explanation are in fact either false or hedged; and the logic of explanation ought to take this into account. Explanations that are grounded on hedged statements *can* be assessed by a critic; the implicational model simply makes explicit where the major burden of the assessment rests: namely, on the question of the truth of falsehood of the bypassing clause. In our view, then, a proposed explanation is subject to rejection on empirical grounds which are not located in the account of explanation provided by the deductive model. But of course those explanations that conform to the deductive model are also subject to empirical refutation, so in this respect the implicational model contains no innovations.

As I have indicated, one motive for proposing this rather more complex version of the deductive model is to provide a pattern that makes explicit the special features of some explanations in biological theory. We shall now consider only historical explanations.

It has sometimes been argued that in their case the deductive model does not apply, because historical explanations fail to cite sufficient conditions of the explanadum, but only temporally antecedent conditions that are in some sense—a sense not well understood—causally connected and continuous with the phenomenon to be explained. And if we do examine historical explanations as they actually occur in biology, not to mention human history and the social sciences, it appears that sufficient conditions are never, or virtually never, mentioned. Moreover, no defender of the deductive model has succeeded in producing a single plausible example of a historical explanation, expanded with the help of laws, that fully meets the deducibility requirement. The implicational model, however, overcomes this difficulty. It makes explicit the way in which generalities on the one hand—our hedged statements—and particular judgments on the other—bypassing statements—are put together into arguments that do provide sufficient conditions of the explanadum and thus qualify, so far, as sound explanations. Of course, the actual explanations that we encounter in biological literature are not fully spelled out; in science, as in everyday life, we seldom offer the grounds of implications unless our arguments are challenged. The implicational model is a recipe for spelling out historical explanations; the deductive model is not.

The general statements employed as grounds in historical explanations are often so trivial and commonplace that mentioning them would be an insult to any reader. Nevertheless, they are not unimportant. Implication is a quasi-formal relation; this large body of trivialities is precisely what puts us in a position to evaluate many implications as if their only dubious aspect were the formal relation of entailment.

Moreover, there are an endless number of trivialities. And although any one of them may hardly be worth mentioning, the judicious selection of a few related ones may provide just the illumination that writers seek in offering historical explanations. An account of the general pattern of explanation should provide places for inserting these trivialities and should show how they are interrelated when the upshot is a genuine explanation rather than a string of clichés.

In addition, however, to commonplace generalities, the biological sciences employ many statements that, although they are not trivialities, hardly merit the honorary title of "law of nature." These statements are the results of painstaking research, and may even be the foundations of biological revolutions. These concern regularities that nevertheless show exceptions. Sometimes, indeed, they are referred to as "laws"—for example, Darwin's laws of replacement and succession, Von Baer's laws, the law of independent assortment, and so on. Sometimes they are referred to as "rules" or merely as statements of trends or tendencies—for example, Bergmann's rule, Dollo's rule, and the tendency of domesticated animals to vary indefinitely from the ancestral type. More often, however, these general statements have no recognized title; they are simply the things we all learn when we learn the "principles" of a science—for instance, that fish in swift streams are not shaped like perch, that the ductus arteriosus atrophies after birth, that haemophilia is inherited, and so on and on.

As I have said, such statements constitute the fabric of whole sciences. They all have exceptions; sometimes we can explain the exceptions, sometimes we cannot. The exceptions are far from negligible, but they do not disqualify the general statements from use in explanations and, indeed, in many cases, from playing the role in explanation assigned to laws in the deductive model. Their use in historical explanation and their pre-eminent role in biology are not exhibited in the deductive model. It is necessary that we explicitly provide a place for hedged statements and for the statements that disclaim reliance on the emergency exit provided by hedging clauses.

15 PSYCHOLOGISM AND METHODOLOGICAL INDIVIDUALISM

Sidney Morgenbesser

The thesis that psychology is the basic social science, a thesis frequently referred to as psychologism, has led a charmed life. So has its sister thesis, methodological individualism, a view perhaps best described as maintaining that all statements about social groups and collectivities are reducible to statements about human beings and, of course, their interrelations. Despite their repeated ostensible refutations, both theses are still very much with us. Professors Popper, Hayek, Nagel, and other distinguished philosophers and social scientists are continuing the debate about them, a debate to which Hume, Hill, Marx, Dewey, Weber, and Freud, among others, have contributed from the time of Plato.

This long and celebrated controversy invites but eludes simple philosophical summary and assessment. For, as is often the case with prolonged methodological disputes, far too many issues have been raised to permit such casual treatment. And so, confronted with a familiar state of affairs, I shall employ an equally familiar strategy and try to distinguish between the various issues and problems. The hope, of course, is that at least partial agreement will follow clarification.

One aim of methodological individualism is easily enough explained. Philosophers and scientists have repeatedly attempted to replace theories and theses that are false or meaningless with others that are meaningful and hopefully true. Of course, replacement programs of this sort are undertaken when it is understood that the original statements have some point or perform some function within the sciences; otherwise there would be little reason to be concerned with them. But though the original statements to be replaced are not devoid of value, those who seek to replace them hope that the substituted statements, which are clearer and more cogent, have greater value. Thus, scientists have often tried to replace statements which seem to countenance space, time, and energy as entities with statements about spatial and temporal relations between entities or events and with statements about powers and capacities of objects and systems to undergo and institute certain types of change. Replacement programs have exercised the minds of the greatest philosophers and physicists from the time of Leibnitz to our own day.

It is therefore not surprising that methodological individualists have also attempted to replace misleading statements in the social sciences with others about individuals which they hope are not misleading but clear and possibly true. *Prima facie* there seems to be some point to their program as well as some need for it. For despite repeated warnings about reification, many social scientists still treat such terms as "culture," "ego," and "value" as if they denoted entities which had causal power and which interacted with and directed peoples and groups. Of course, some perspective is necessary. Statements such as "people have value" can be as innocent as the statement "he gave him a dirty look," but if I interpret the latter to mean "he had a look, it was dirty and he gave it to him," I would most likely be dismissed as trying to make a bad joke. But Professor N. Smelser is not joking when he says, "A society is not, however, a simple conglomeration of activities, roles, and collectivities. At a higher level it is subject to a number of controls. It is governed by a value system which defines and legitimates the activities of the social system." The methodological individualist objects not only because a dubious entity—a value system—has been invoked, but also because a spurious explanation has been offered. Why are certain actions considered justified and legitimate in a given society? The value system justifies; this is the answer suggested by Professor Smelser, and it is no help. He seems to have concluded from the thesis that the attitudes and beliefs of people are systematically inter-related to the one that there is a system which has its own properties and which is engaged in its own actions. Shades of absolute idealism.

Seeking clarity, therefore, the methodological individualist suggests that the social scientists begin—logically, not chronologically—with statements about human individuals and then introduce others that can be reduced to statements about human individuals; reduced in the sense of being shown to be equal in truth value, not in meaning with statements about individuals and relationships between them. Alternatively, the methodological individualist seems to claim that all statements in the social sciences are reducible in the manner he indicates. Of course, here the phrase "in the social sciences" is not to be taken too literally, for I assume that the methodological individualist does not want to defend the silly thesis that all sentences about physical objects used by the social scientist and that all mathematical theorems employed by the latter are reducible to the sort of statements the methodological individualist specifies.

Common sense indicates therefore that methodological individualism is to be construed as a thesis about all true and scientifically useful theories and sentences introduced by the social scientist, not as a thesis about all sentences he uses, many of which have been borrowed from elsewhere, e.g., physics and mathematics. Observe that the phrase "true or useful" indicates that the methodological individualist will most likely have a double standard and will not necessarily seek to banish or replace all non-true social scientific theories. It is a commonplace that economic theory is replete with false—or to use the description liked by Milton Freedman, not realistic—statements but which are useful for the purposes of prediction and calculation. I presume that the methodological individualist will not attempt the impossible, a reduction of such statements to true statements about individuals, and will be sober enough to accept these statements merely as useful myths. Observe that in these cases no one is fooled or misled and hence the tolerance of a methodological individualist.

Of course, his tolerance has limits, and, as I understand him, the methodological individualist would not tolerate theories which countenance forces of history, spirits of the times, and super-organic cultures. His tolerance ends because of his conviction that such theories cannot be used for the purposes of prediction, much less explanation. Here he may be wrong, but he is not guilty of the arrogance of accepting only those statements which are capable of reduction to the type of statement he prefers and dismissing as nonsensical all statements which are not capable of reduction, simply because they are capable of such reduction.

But which statements will the methodological individualist not merely tolerate, but accept as meaningful and possibly true? In particular, will he tolerate statements about abstract entities, meanings, universals, rules? To some, the question is silly. The methodological individualist is a nominalist; otherwise, why his emphasis upon statements about specific human individuals and relations between them? Reasoning in this manner, Professor M. R. Cohen classified the methodological individualist of his day, the legal realist, as a nominalist, and criticized him for not being able to offer a satisfactory analysis of the nature of legal phenomena. Would that Professor Cohen's convictions were sharable. I have already noted that the methodological individualist accepts much of classical mathematics which is not nominalistic and hence that it is not obvious that the methodological individualist is a nominalist. In point of fact, Professor K. Popper, who is a strong defender of methodological individualism, is to the best of my knowledge opposed to nominalism and so are others but, to be sure, not all defenders of methodological individualism. Neither can I share Professor Cohen's conviction that a nominalist cannot with a suitable interpretation provide a satisfactory interpretation of the nature of legal phenomena. But to discuss nominalism here is not my aim; I wanted merely to indicate a gap in the methodological individualist's position. He is, qua methodological individualism not clear and explicit on the currently much discussed issue (at least by philosophers) —of the need for abstract entities in an adequate theory of human action and belief and hence cannot be considered as having offered an all embracing methodological postulate for the interpretation of social scientific theories.

Still, methodological individualism may be an important though limited thesis if it is interpreted, as my introductory remarks suggested, as a thesis about groups and people or as a thesis about theories and statements about them. Unfortunately, even if we restrict the thesis in this way, all is not clear sailing; the methodological individualist owes a specification of the types of predicates or descriptions of individual human beings he will accept as clear enough for theory construction. We have noted and applauded the opposition of methodological individualists to reification and to the postulation of dubious entities. It is only fair to add that one may avoid the sins denounced by a methodological individualist and make no substantial progress. One for whom superegos do not exist need not accept with equanimity the use of the term "guided by his superego," though its application to Mr. Jones requires us to grant the existence only of Mr. Jones, not both of Mr. Jones and his superego. But here many would say there is no pressing problem; the suggestion that leaps to their mind is that the methodological individualist will or should accept as basic statements which are about the observable behavior of individuals or statements which contain, and contain essentially, only such observational and behavioristic predicates. Since "guided by his superego" does not seem to be such a predicate, the methodological individualist may at least question its acceptability.

Construed this way, methodological individualism seems sane and moreover distinct from psychologism, distinct on the proviso that not all behavioristic predicates are construed as psychological ones. All, to the advantage of methodological individualism, claim some of its defenders, e.g., Professor Popper. Psychologism, he believes, has been shown to be impossible by Marx; methodological individualism, being distinct, survives the Marxian revolution in the social sciences. But, even if we grant this claim, which I will examine below, we need not grant much more. For the methodological individualist seems to have shifted his emphasis from statements about individuals to statements about observable behavior, and hence he has not distinguished his position from classical empiricism. His thesis seems to be a version of empiricism and not a new and independent thesis. Moreover, it is a dubious version, for it seems to presuppose the debatable thesis that observational predicates apply only to individuals and not to groups. (Consider the term "is unruly" applied to a group.) Moreover, it is not at all evident that any interesting or relevant social scientific predicate can be defined only by reference to what a person does if by doing we mean "moving his limbs." When a man signs a check he does not do two things, move his hands and also sign a check; moving his hand in certain ways under certain circumstances is signing a check. But still the phrase "signed a check" is not behavioristic or for that matter purely observational; its application requires either assumptions or knowledge about a man's intentions and the social circumstances under which he executed his intention.

Confronted with the latter objection, the methodological individualist makes either one of two moves. He might insist that such phrases as "signed a check" are clearly observational ones, though to be sure in an extended sense of observational; he might insist that a social scientist should not begin with such phrases as "signed a check," "voted," "bought a paper" but with more basic behavioristic ones and introduce others as needed. But either way there is little progress as the difficulties with the first suggestion—which are matched by difficulties with the second—show. The problem is, of course, the well-known one that theoretical social scientific statements even about individuals, which appear to be both true and useful, are not reducible to statements about the observable behavior of individuals, at least not reducible in the manner required by the methodological individualist. Linguistics is replete with statements about the various rules that a person has learned, and sociology, with statements about a person's attitude which, though possibly confirmable by statements about the behavior of individuals, are certainly not equivalent in meaning or truth value to them. The methodological individualist can, of course, save his thesis and insist that all theories in the social sciences which are true and useful are ultimately confirmed by statements about the observable behavior of human beings. But then, I think, he has trivialized his position and, moreover, is silent on many of the intriguing questions in the social sciences. Thus, we would have expected his thesis to shed some light on the conceptual interconnections between micro- and macro-economic theories in the social sciences; now his position does not. Since both are confirmed by statements about individuals, the methodological individualist accepts both and analyzes neither.

Note that I have not attempted to refute methodological individualism; I have merely claimed that the methodological individualist cannot identify his thesis with the trite one that all true and useful statements are confirmed by statements about individuals. I agree, however, that the methodological individualist may someday specify a class of predicates and show that all true and useful statements in the social sciences are reducible to statements which contain such predicates and hence save his thesis. But, until he does, we must credit him only with a promise, not with a fulfillment.

My tentative conclusion would be challenged by many critics of methodological individualism on the grounds that the latter thesis entails the patent falsehood that groups are not real and that social collectivities are mere epiphenomena. Why this charge, which has repeatedly been made—often by extreme Hegelians, but just as often by sober Aristotelians? The question is appropriate because the charge seems absurd; a methodological individualist does not deny the existence or reality of groups; for him a group is simply a disconnected entity whose parts are distinct human beings and hence is as real as an individual composed of interconnected parts. The methodological individualist might moreover grant that groups have properties of their own which individuals do not have, perhaps emergent ones. He would, however, add that there is no mystery or difficulty for him since he is claiming that statements about groups are equivalent in truth value, not in meaning to statements about individuals that compose them. Perhaps an analogy might help. A conjunction of two sentences has the property of being true if and only if both members of the conjunction are true, but neither conjunct has that property. Yet the truth of the conjunction is determined by the truth of the conjuncts.

Our question and puzzlement continue; why, given its patent falsehood, the recurrent objection to the methodological individualist on the grounds that he does not recognize the existence or reality of groups? Two answers suggest themselves, one ideological and the other methodological. The charge may have resulted from a confusion between moral and methodological individualism and a desire to defeat both in one fell swoop. Moral individualism maintains that all social institutions are to be justified by their effect on individuals whose utilities are paramount, a moral view which some Hegelians mistakenly attempt to refute by noting that since individuals are not real—that is, not self-sufficient and can develop only with a society—it follows that society is morally superior to men. One might as well argue that oxygen is morally superior to man. Issues about moral individualism aside, note that Hegelians and others who use the term "real" metaphysically and as equivalent to "self-sufficient" and "self-determined" are not therefore contradicting the methodological individualist who is, as already noted, using the term "real" in another and indeed innocuous sense. For the latter to say X is real is to say there are X's, not that the X's are self-sufficient. But though there is no conflict and in principle one can use the term "real" in both the innocuous and the metaphysical sense, the advantage is clearly with the former one. The latter, I think, has no application, and introducing it allows us to disguise a platitude as a profundity. The cash value of the trite observation that human beings do not, and most likely cannot, develop their human traits in isolation is not increased by its rephrasal as an assertation about the unreality of individuals. Directed against certain metaphysical views, the thesis I am supporting seems obvious. But in a less obvious way it controverts more plausible-sounding but equally dubious views which maintain that the group or society is prior to the individual.

But still, as already suggested, there may be one good methodological reason for denying that groups are real. On occasion we might insist that a term A is not lawlike because we cannot discover interesting laws about those entities picked out by that term, and, if we are convinced that this is the case, we may then perhaps in an exaggerated way say that A-type entities are not real, but simply conventionally grouped together. Perhaps then those who, like the anthropologist B. Malinowski, say that groups are not real mean that we will not find interesting general laws about groups and that it would be, for example, a mistake to seek to confirm statements of the form "all groups of the type P are of type Q." Now, if this is the thesis at stake when discussion of the reality of groups is raised, methodological individualists need not dissent from it. But neither must they accept it.

Therefore, I think that Professor Popper, in his influential book *The Open Society*, and others are mistaken when they suggest that a methodological individualist cannot accept a holistic approach to society and must deny, for example, that there are laws of the form "if society of type A exists at time T, it will be followed by a society of type B," where A and B stand in place of predicates that apply to society as a whole. He can accept them and, with Dilehey and others, view societies as processes, historical ones, and even seek to discover the laws, if any, which describe such a process, and then of course try to reduce such lawful statements to others. But whether he will succeed even to specify the type of statements to which he will reduce the others is as already stated an open question.

Some of these objections to methodological individualism also apply to psychologism. As was the case with methodological individualism, we may demand that the defender of psychologism present us with a theory or decision about the meaningfulness of scientific terms and also request that he be explicit as to what social scientific theories he admits as candidates for reduction to psychological ones. But there is no need to emphasize these objections; there is a more obvious and pressing one. The defender of psychologism must at least present us with a criterion or sketch of one that will allow us to distinguish between psychological and non-psychological theories; otherwise the debate about psychologism may not be resolvable. Here it might be thought that no special criterion for use of the term psychological theory is needed and that ordinary usage can serve as a guide. But this is not the case. Psychology is on occasion identified as a science of the individual and on other occasions as a science of the mental or the private, but obviously neither characterization is helpful. It is apparent that not all terms that apply to individuals are psychological predicates, and it is equally obvious that much of contemporary psychological theory does not deal with the mental or the private. Neither would it be useful to identify the psychological with the intentional or the motivated and then specify psychologism as maintaining that all social scientific explanations are ultimately motivational only, or explanations that account for social events by reference to the intentions of agents and can be exhaustively explained by them. Sociologists have often insisted that much in social life is unanticipated; psychologists do not explain the acquisition of motives by insisting that we are motivated to acquire them.

Of course one can arbitrarily specify or predict a criterion for the use of the term psychological and then insist that all social scientific theories can be reduced to psychological ones in this sense. But, since such arbitrary specifications may be presented without limit, there is no way of clearly and definitively discussing them. All that one may suggest is that we do not arbitrarily dismiss them before they are elaborated.

In view of these difficulties, we may be tempted to dismiss the entire controversy about psychologism as devoid of interest and beyond debate. But this dismissal is, I think, premature. We might understand this controversy if we review it historically and begin with what I shall call the eighteenth-century version of psychologism.

Many eighteenth-century writers, including Montesquieu, Condillac, Hume, and Condorcet, suggested the program for finding general laws and principles in the light of which we might understand the varieties of human behavior and diversities of cultures. Montesquieu and others suggested hypotheses and schematic expressions in which such complex predicates as "monarchy" and "republic" appeared. Others wanted mere fundamental principles. Since the name "psychology" had not yet been invented, these writers referred to such principles either as metaphysical ones or as principles of human nature. Oversimplifying a complicated story, we may say that two such types of laws were suggested, the French and the Scottish. These sets of principles frequently overlapped, and some thinkers such as Hume vacillated from one to the other. We shall focus our interest chiefly on the latter set of principles, the Scottish.

The following four substantive assumptions and one methodological assumption figured essentially in the Scottish position:

169

(a) A set of assumptions about the association of ideas and the association of impressions.
(b) A set of assumptions about the conditions under which we experience certain emotions.
(c) A set of assumptions about the expression of these emotions.
(d) A set of assumptions about motives.

The methodological assumption about rationality is difficult to specify in detail. These philosophers did not assert that all human beings are rational, but they did proceed as if they believed that the best way to explain social institutions was to exhibit them as means for certain ends. They did not, of course, assume that we decide upon our means in that manner. McDougall's assertion that those who came before him had written as if everything were to be explained by thinking is misleading.

In developing the four assumptions, various eighteenth-century thinkers assumed that certain types of situations naturally elicited certain types of emotions; certain types of emotions were naturally expressed in certain ways; and certain motives were natural or innate and others acquired as a result of or through association.

If we grant these four substantive hypotheses and the one methodological assumption, the procedure of eighteenth-century psychologists is clear. First, given any drive or emotion, they undertook to find out whether it was innate or acquired. If innate or original, they attempted to explain the derivation by reference to the laws of association of ideas and impressions. Second, they exhibited any institution as a means for the satisfaction of some human desire, whether natural or acquired. There was, of course, no assumption that all institutions satisfied the desires that ought to be gratified. It was assumed, for example, by some thinkers such as Voltaire, who was influenced by this approach, that the church merely satisfied the desires of the priesthood and otherwise had no utility.

The program was, of course, never carried out. We shall discuss three of the reasons for this failure. In the first place, these men never had any method for distinguishing the desires, passions, and abilities which are native from those which are not.

Hume, for example, at one time attempted to explain the genesis of sympathy, but later asserted that we must stop somewhere in our explanations; that it is not probable that sympathy can be received into principles more simple and universal, whatever attempts have been made to that purpose.

Second, many of these men were moralists and turned quickly from the task of analyzing in detail the specific desires satisfied by specific institutions to the task of formulating a system of rules to make men virtuous and happy. David Fordyce, a lesser-known member of the Scottish school, is revealing when he writes, "Moral philosophy contemplates human nature, its moral powers and connections, and from these deduces the laws of action. . . . It is denominated an art, as it contains a system of rules for becoming virtuous and happy."

Third, the second part of their program did not prove to be a useful guide for inquiry. Eighteenth-century thinkers were able to specify the interrelationships between desires and institutions if, and only if, the institutions were described very generally. Thus Hume set out to specify the interrelationships between the desire to maximize utility and the institution of property. But he was not able to account for the difference in property rights and the conceptions of private property that existed from society to society.

But many philosophers and social scientists have not merely observed that the program failed, but have insisted that it was wrong in principle.

According to many thinkers, such as Marx, Dewey, Collingwood, and others, the eighteenth-century psychologist was wrong because he had no sense of history, did not realize that psychological phenomena are dependent upon social and cultural ones, and, in general, overlooked the importance of cultural variations.

Some of these critics went further and often insisted that sociology is autonomous and that psychological phenomena are to be explained by reference to social ones rather than vice versa. These claims are so familiar and seemingly so persuasive that many distinguished philosophers have granted them. Thus Professor Popper has maintained that Marx's greatest contribution to the social sciences was his reasoned establishment of the thesis of the autonomy of sociology.

Here Professor Popper and others are, I think, in error and overlook the obvious limitations of sociologism. Marx, as many of his recent commentators have emphasized, did not think that a theory of man is completely dependent upon or consists of sociological premises. Durkheim and Devey attempted to establish the independence of sociology from psychology, but failed. The latter failed because he assumed that psychological phenomena result from the interaction between culture and human nature, but never showed how to distinguish between them and was not too explicit about his use of the term "culture." He advised his readers that his use of "culture" was analogous to that of the anthropologists. But anthropological usage is not too helpful, as we can see from an examination of the following typical anthropological specification. "By 'culture' we understand," writes Professor R. H. Lowie, "the sum total of what an individual acquires from his society." To assert that behavior is influenced by culture and then to assert that "culture" designates all acquired behavioral traits is misleading.

In view of these difficulties with sociology, it is not at all surprising that psychologism has had a revival. Recently, it has taken the shape that learning theory is the basic theory and that learning theorists can explain why people behave the way they do: they learn to behave that way.

But though all of this may seem promising, there are difficulties which may be indicated if we heed a particular learning theory, one developed by the late Prof. R. L. Hull and which is still of some interest.

Learning theorists believe that they can explain why people behave as they do. People are influenced by their parents because they learn from them. Stated so boldly, the answer seems singularly devoid of merit, but it involves much of interest and importance.

Classical psychologism insisted that certain dispositions are universal: for example, the disposition to be angry when insulted, to minimize happiness, and so on. Marx, Dewey, and others denied this. Although this denial was not startling, it is surprising that they offered so little in the way of an explanation of the diversities of behavior. Contemporary psychologism agrees with the Deweyan critique. Adherents to contemporary psychologism insist that the particular dispositions to which classical psychologism called our attention are not universal. But, if I understand them correctly, they believe that they have discovered other dispositions which are universal. We may not all love money or the chase, but we all learned to love money or the chase in the same manner. Laws of learning are universal laws, and with them, plus knowledge of relevant conditions, we can account for the diversities. But there are some problems.

In the first place, Hull frequently explains how a disposition is acquired. To do so, he does not think it necessary to explain how a response was first made. Given that a response occurred and that it was reinforced, then, other things being equal, we will tend to develop certain habits. But although Hull does not see the need of explaining the original response, it is clear that a complete psychology must explain not merely the repetition and the acquisition but the genesis of responses.

Second, suppose a certain response is reinforced and learning takes place. Why is that response reinforced? A learning theorist of Hullian persuasion tells us that when a Jewish child is first presented with a book, he will be asked to taste some honey that has been put on the book. As a result, he will acquire a disposition to like books. The psychologists no doubt did not intend this as an explanation of the traditional Jewish love for learning. But if the explanation was accepted, the question still remains, why did the Jews reinforce a response to books? Why did they not reinforce the response of a child to meat after it drank milk? To say that is their culture will send us back to the difficulties which we faced when considering Dewey.

Even if psychologists find the basic laws of learning—and I do not believe that they have found them yet—it is clear that from such laws we could not explain why a certain set of cultural conditions obtained at any given time.

If we consider the latter question irrelevant and accept the view that the task of the learning theorist is not that of explaining the genesis and constitution of culture, then we are forced to the conclusion that certain social scientific data fall outside the scope of learning theory and, consequently, that the thesis that psychology is the basic social science must be abandoned.

Is psychology the basic social science? The answer is, I think, in the negative if we identify psychology with learning theory and hence claim that all social scientific theories can be reduced to learning theory or at least one of its variants. But this is a narrow identification; learning theory is not even all of psychology. What then is the science of psychology? As I have tried to show, "psychology" has been continually redefined and apparently reserved in advance for the name of that science, if any, to which all social scientific ones will be reduced. Of course, this is primarily true of defenders of psychologism, and hence the latter thesis may very well be self-saving.

16 SCIENCE, FACT, AND VALUE

Michael Scriven

INTRODUCTION

A certain mental picture of the *relation between* value judgments (as opposed to their intrinsic nature) dominates much methodological discussion of values and distorts the reality. It is widely supposed that a man's system of values can be thought of as a pyramidical hierarchy, and, conversely, as a tree structure. These have, at one end, a large number of specific practical values (liking today's issue of *The Times,* preferring one's nephew James to the neighbors' Johnny, and so forth) which are justifiable by, or derivable from, a smaller number of more general values (liking the most compendious paper in the country and not caring that it also has the most typographical errors, liking little boys who are intelligent but rather quiet), which are themselves instances of still fewer and more general values (liking the qualities of being well informed, intelligent, secure). Now if this were a realistic account, all one's values would derive from a relatively small number of "highest" (or "most basic") values, which by definition are not derived from any other values. Where do *they* come from? It seems very plausible—if one is thinking in terms of this model—to suppose that they must be simply a free choice by the individual. The model cuts them off from any visible means of support, and in doing so it misrepresents the extensive interaction between values and experience that actually exists. In the following section we shall discuss a more appropriate model.

A CONSTRUCTIVE ACCOUNT OF
THE FACT/VALUE RELATIONSHIP

Values in the extended sense consist in or arise from needs and wants in the narrow sense. The primary type of value is something that is directly needed or wanted. Secondary values arise because we have to set up certain intermediate goals if we are to achieve the primary goals. The most important secondary or instrumental value is rationality, an attitude which is a method, a method which maximizes the efficiency of our attempts to achieve our primary goals. Optimization requires that we also be prepared to adjust our primary goals, where this is psychologically possible, in the light of the constraints of external and internal reality limitations. External limitations arise from the unavailability of goods, the opposition of others, and so on; internal ones arise from conflict between different goals or difficulties due to character defects. The whole vocabulary of value is generated by the attempt to communicate about, and to structure and refine communications about, this interaction of means and ends, and means that become ends, and the facts about them.

The language and logic of value can be applied to any situations exhibiting the characteristics we have just described; thus we may talk of good and bad, better and best, ought and should and is, in a context of grading examination papers, bassoons, chess openings, the Alexandria Quartet, and the nobility of actions. The relevant criteria in each case are different—what makes a bassoon good is not what makes an act noble—but it is inappropriate to describe this variation as a sign that the word "good" is ambiguous or is being used in a different sense or with a different meaning. "Good," like the other terms of the evaluation vocabulary, is a function word and not a labeling word like "red."

We do not say that the word "conclusion" (of an argument) is ambiguous because quite different kinds of statements can be conclusions, or because what would count as a sound conclusion in the context of legal evidence would not so count in the context of mathematical logic. The point about the term "conclusion" is that it stands for any consequence that may legitimately be inferred by whatever standards of inference are justifiable in the particular context of the discussion. It no more has to stand for deductive implications alone than the word "dog" has to stand for poodles alone. And similarly "good" has no primary commitment to the moral use; it always serves the same function, that of indicating entities which score well on the relevant evaluation criteria, whatever they may be. The process of evaluation, being simply the combination of goal criteria with objectively determined performance measures, in general involves only empirical and analytical procedures, though certainly it involves more than simple observation.

In the special case of moral evaluation, special criteria are involved. The only defensible set of such criteria are complex compounds of the welfare variables of the population on which the morality is based. The ultimate foundation of morality is the most basic needs and wants of men. Although the utilitarian formula for compounding the individual welfare functions is both crucially ambiguous and mistaken in being too limited in its range of application, the spirit of its approach is the right one in its concern with utility, although it is deficient in its safeguards for justice. But these conclusions about morality, which are controversial among moral philosophers, are not crucial for what has been said about value judgments in general, and indeed if we make certain other plausible assumptions, are not even essential in order to justify the use of the same approach in the field of morality. For the above analysis leads to basic principles that are very similar to those in several more traditional approaches, and the practical applications of all should thus be closely similar, if applied equally rationally.

If one is prepared to accept, on whatever meta-ethical basis, the proposition that morality definitionally or even fundamentally involves the notion of equality of men's rights, then one need accept no other independent principle or criterion, for the other standard moral principles and values (justice, honesty, and so on) can be derived therefrom with the assistance of some rather simple facts about human nature. And moral evaluation simply becomes evaluation of acts, directed by the ultimate criterion of equality of consideration, or by the proximate criteria of justice, honesty, and so forth when these are more readily applicable and not in dispute. The morality of particular practices, such as monogamy or polygamy, then emerges as defensible in certain environments and not in others, whereas the more general principles of morality derive from more nearly universal features of the human situation.

Accepting the equality criterion as defining or generating morality—like accepting any other criterion—does not entail accepting the legitimacy of moral claims upon one's attention. But it does make it possible to see moral value judgments as just one group in the range of evaluating activities, which may or may not be of any personal interest, from evaluating driving skills to male ballet dancers, each based on comprehensible and applicable criteria—although these criteria may be applied only by exercising hard-earned skills. The question of *justifying* the principle of equal rights, or attention to it, is a different question, and one that will not be taken up in detail here beyond remarking that attention to comparative anthropology, and to those problems of game theory which can be solved only by co-operative strategies, provides us with strong grounds for supposing that enforcement and even acceptance of morality can perform a valuable function in improving welfare. It should be clear from these analogies that the question of justification is, on this account, largely a question for the social sciences, whether or not it has previously been accepted as part of their province.

An important consequence of the preceding account of value judgments is their previously mentioned derivative character: they arise only from the interaction of *pre-existing* wants or needs with external and internal restraints. There is nothing intrinsically good or bad about the original wants or needs, although the constraints on and the interactions between them may lead to a *subsequent* overall evaluation in terms of which some of the original goals must be regarded as less important, not feasible, or disadvantageous, and hence devalued. No outside source of values is necessary for this to occur; we rightly regard heavy smoking as a bad habit to acquire because we know that a slice of life is usually more important to most people than the pleasure of inhaling smoke. It follows that whenever welfare will be served by an action, there is automatically a reason for doing it, without any need for proof that it is good to serve welfare in this way.

It isn't intrinsically good or bad to serve welfare (one's own or that of others); it's simply something one has a good reason to do. One may subsequently discover overriding reasons to do otherwise, but at this stage there exists one good reason in favor of this particular action. Consequently, the tendency of the value-allergic social scientist to withhold a value judgment which is clearly supported by extensive available evidence, on the grounds that it *might* be wrong to seek welfare in this case, manifests an exaggerated skepticism. Welfare-promoting is self-justifying until shown wrong—that is, shown to be inconsistent with other, more important, values derived from welfare-promoting. Wholesale skepticism about value judgments is as absurd as wholesale skepticism about observation claims. One does not have to believe that any particular ones are indubitable in order to be certain that many are true, and confident enough of some to act on them.

Even if we assume that value judgments are logically more complex than observations (which is certainly false of some primary, first-person, value claims), total skepticism about value judgments is just as absurd as the suggestion that one can *only* be sure of observations and hence should never make assertions about the *explanations* or *predictions* of eclipses or atomic explosions. The average explanation or prediction may be a little more fallible than the average observation, but it is still often strong enough to stake one's life on, as one does every moment of the day, and the same is true of value judgments. It is important to see that although the variables bearing on a value judgment are quite often, in a practical situation, undeterminable for the time being, just as the facts needed to settle on the right explanation may be unavailable, one can *not* conclude that this is always or necessarily true. Where the variables are undeterminable, an interim evaluation of various actions in the light of this uncertainty is not in the least weakened by the impossibility of making the hoped-for kind of evaluation. Before

179

turning to an example to illustrate this point, we conclude the general discussion of a value system with an alternative to the pyramidical, hierarchical, or tree-structure account of the relation between values.

The best model for a value system is a web or net of webs stretched across the ground of experience, serving as one of the structures that unifies it. The intersections or points of termination of strands represent values, the strands themselves represent empirical or logical connections. The more important values serve as the focus for many strands of the web, and are not necessarily anchored to the ground. The peripheral strands—and *some* internal ones—terminate in points of attachment to the ground which represent the most specific applications of the value system. The net is extended by the enlargement of experience, which brings with it the need for new choices, that is, new tie-points at the periphery. The selection of these is governed by the general principle of organization of the net, which is roughly the principle of maximizing strength by minimizing strain. A particular series of choices at the periphery can set up a considerable asymmetrical strain on the net which will either leave it in a weakened condition or lead to substantial readjustment of the internal organization. Similarly, examination of internal structure may uncover purely internal strains that can be relieved by altering the relationships—the interconnections of the internal nodes.

This model is deployed in a very different way from the tree/pyramid. There is no single trunk/apex; but there is recognition of the fact that some values are considerably more general than others. The impact of experience is felt throughout the system and not just at one end. The constant process of adjustment is represented more realistically, with experience operating on values at all levels; after all, experience sometimes obliges us to make choices between alternatives couched in very general terms. The connections between values of different levels of generality in the net model, as in reality, are not always through the same intermediary values. The more crucial values can be seen as deriving their status from the attempt to reduce the tensions imposed by particular choices rather than being the primary source from which the particular choices flow; but the element of truth in the latter view is preserved in the description of the way in which a new anchor point is selected.

THE EFFECTS OF EMPIRICAL UNCERTAINTY

It is important to stress again that even uncertainty about various crucial facts does not entail a corresponding uncertainty in all relevant recommendations. It may mean that a *final* recommendation cannot be made, but typically an *interim* recommendation of great reliability is possible—for example, the recommendation that no action should be taken until more data are available. On other occasions, the degree of uncertainty may be swamped by other considerations and even a direct recommendation may still be possible.

A good example is the tariff problem in economics. There are many occasions when the decision whether to increase a tariff barrier properly depends on a very complicated estimate of the relative importance to the potential domestic consumer of (a) lower prices for a useful imported commodity and the attendant consequences of increased international trade, as against (b) greater stability in the domestic economy with its attendant gains of a better long-term guarantee of the availability of the (admittedly more expensive) domestic product and a better short-term employment situation, and so forth. The attempt to give a definite and demonstrably correct answer to such a problem is indeed a forbidding one, further clouded by the dependence of an answer upon unreliable long-range predictions as to the political repercussions of the alternative actions. But there are plenty of engineering and medical phenomena for which explanations cannot now be given with any reliability—for example, many of the crashes of the big jets, or the more general phenomenon of the efficacy of Graafian ring contraceptives. No one concludes that all explanations in general, or even *these* explanations, are essentially inaccessible or essentially matters of opinion. In certain *specific* tariff disputes, the balance of known advantages for a particular decision simply swamps the alternative in the sense that *none of the probable values* of the unknown variables would provide enough weight to alter the balance of consideration. In such cases the proper conclusion is simply that on the evidence available, so-and-so must be recommended. The provisos that the evidence may change, and that the conclusion is less than mathematically certain, are superfluous because they are footnotes to almost any scientific conclusion.

THE EFFECTS OF VALUE-ALLERGY

A typical instance of such a conclusion arises where a small industry, absolutely vital for defense purposes, is faced with immediate and irreversible extinction unless competition from a foreign source is reduced sharply—the precision optical industry has been in this situation in the past. In a world where the possibility of war is quite significant, there can be no doubt of the proper answer. There are many situations where the trained eye and the analytical tools of the economist will uncover an equally certain decision from a mass of figures that the lay government official cannot interpret. It is nonsensical for the economist to turn shy at this point and refuse to draw the obvious conclusion. Indeed, standard government practice is increasingly to call him in as a specialist to *make* recommendations in such cases. The power and legitimacy of these is currently masked by the value-free myth, the mystique of the managerial decision. Of course, the "decision," where this means the responsibility, must be managerial—or presidential, or legislative—but the fact that only the executive can legitimately make the decision in no way supports the view that only he can legitimately recommend.

A clear example of the improprieties consequent upon these misunderstandings arises in the tariff issue over the fact that direct subsidy to the affected industry is nearly always preferable to a raised tariff barrier. It is more specific, it is more honest (the taxpayer knows just how much aid is costing him), it is more easily modifiable (usually unaffected by international treaty), and so on. But the lobbies continually pressure the executive and legislative branches into tariff changes that are contrary to the best interests of the population as a whole, and their success in doing so is surely partly due to the passive acceptance by the populus, and the lack of rejection by the professional economists, of the idea that such issues of policy are somehow best decided by the government. Of course, they must be *executed* by the government, but in cases like the one just described, it is sometimes simply a sign of incompetence if not malfeasance for the executive branch to evaluate the issue and in this sense decide what is best. For none of the relevant considerations are inaccessible to the economist and some are too technical to be easily appreciated by someone without training in economics.

There are indeed many areas of decision where the representatives of a government are best able to determine the values of those with whom it is negotiating and where the decisions it must make are crucially dependent upon those values. In such areas the government *is* the specialist. But the advances of the social sciences and the techniques of communication, with the consequent diminution in the role of the Foreign Service as privileged informants, have shrunk those areas from their vast nineteenth-century expanse. Yet the consequences of this change in the real situation have been masked by the professional confusion over the facts/value distinction. Of course, it is still often the case that "experts" will give conflicting testimony about certain factual matters—for example, the attitude of the Chinese government toward the war in Viet Nam—and the executive must adjudicate between them. In such matters we have not yet achieved substantial reliability. The conflicting recommendations of legal, tax, and fiscal experts called on by a large company are probably no more consistent, yet the company does not suppose it should not use legal experts. There is a tendency to think that if a field of allegedly scientific study cannot produce a single, provably right answer, it can't be a science, and if it isn't a science, then anyone's judgment is as good as anyone else's. But a narrowing down or an enlarging of the possibilities, or a reevaluation of the probabilities, can be a very great step forward and this kind of step is the characteristic unit of progress in the social sciences.

Furthermore, it is *increasingly* the case that the executive will do a poor job even of adjudication unless he has an expert's training. The conception of the ideal executive as someone un-contaminated by the partisan disputes of the specialists must be set against the conception of the incompetent executive as some-one unable to assess the significance of the arguments of the experts. To put the situation bluntly, the best executive is an unprejudiced expert. To the extent that expertise in all the rele-vant fields is an unrealistic goal, the executive must possess the habit of mind of the expert—the needle-sharp critical skills and the aseptic synthesizing capacity of the first-rate scientist—*and* all the general tools of the methodologies of the social sciences. He *must* understand the role and significance of observer bias, projection, matched controls, pilot studies, practice and Haw-thorne and halo effects, survey errors and sampling procedures, minimax and maximin, the voter's paradox, and a hundred more. The executive without scientific training sometimes attains the first criterion, never the second. Social scientists often attain the second, very rarely the first. So a good executive or a good legislator *ought* to be a good social scientist, and since executives and legislators certainly should make decisions, it follows that social scientists should.

REAL-VALUE CLAIMS WITHIN EVERY SCIENCE

Independently of this line of argument—which is a kind of back-door route to the conclusion—there is another way of sup-porting the conclusion at which we are aiming. We have so far proceeded by exhibiting the weaknesses in the attacks on it and showing how a better understanding of the nature of value judg-ments makes it clear that they are wholly composed of elements which the social scientist is best equipped to determine, com-bined in a way which he is again best equipped to understand. This does not show that making value judgments already falls within the presently accepted domain of the social sciences, only that there is an overwhelming case for including it within that domain. We now suggest that it is also possible to show that social scientists must make one very important kind of value judgment just because they are scientists, and *some* of them must make *moral* value judgments because of the particular kind of social science with which they are concerned.

That science, whether pure or applied, necessarily involves *non*-moral value judgments follows immediately from an examination of the scientific procedure of evaluating hypotheses, explanations, theories, experimental designs, lab and field procedures. This is the heart and soul of science, and training the student to good standards and practices in these matters is widely held to be the most important aspect of his scientific apprenticeship. Moreover, there is no way to eliminate the procedure of theory evaluation, for example, in favor of the routine application of some standard test. This is a full-scale evaluation problem with the value base itself open to debate. For the merit of a theory is not equivalent to the number of true predictions it generates, or the number of true explanations, or the extent of the simplification of the data it facilitates (even if there were some useful way to measure such quantities). It is a variably weighted combination of all of these, with the successful predictions, explanations, and simplifications themselves weighted according to importance, and the grand total offset by a weighted measure of the erroneous assertions or impressions. Even to talk in this imprecise way is misleading because it suggests that one could discover a precise formula by some kind of empirical or logical research. But there is no such formula, because the weights are themselves variable, being—rightly—affected by the relative success of different kinds of theories in the rest of science. And even at one particular time, the notion of establishing "the exact quantitative measure of the merit of a theory" is unrealistic because of the many dubious methodological presuppositions that would have to be built into any such measure. Good and bad estimates are possible, but precise ones are not.

The evaluation of theories (or experiments, or interpretations), like the evaluation of used automobiles, can be done expertly or ineptly; it is a skill and not a matter of taste, and it cannot be reduced to a non-evaluative procedure even in the way that leads to valued-performance claims. The scientist, *qua* scientist, must make real-value judgments.

MORAL VALUE CLAIMS IN THE BEHAVIORAL SCIENCES

There are also many areas of applied science—for example, psychotherapy, social work with delinquents, curriculum construction, public health planning, penology, and pedagogy— where *moral* value judgments are unavoidable and the only choice lies between making them rationally and making them haphazardly. (Related considerations apply to history—the history of war, for example.) There will often be room for important differences of opinion on these issues, but this does not mean that neither opinion can be falsified by the facts or future turns of events and—more importantly—it does not mean that there are no cases where the correct value judgment is demonstrable and alternative opinions indefensible.

The best treatment for juvenile delinquents and their parents, on the one hand, is still debatable; but, on the other, the death penalty, for any crime, is indefensible. There is no point in beating about the bush here; with respect to every relevant argument the abolitionists have long since won and only prejudice or ignorance keeps the change from the statute books. The situation might change, as more refined statistics become available, or as a result of more general abolition; but the case for abolition at the moment is better than the case for the special theory of relativity. This is a straightforward value judgment conclusion, against which it is hard to find a single voice raised by anyone with a thorough knowledge of the evidence, an understanding of the law, and any moral concern at all. Is it not part of the province of penology to draw such a conclusion? If not, why not —when the claim is substantiable, the result of a complex inference, and of obvious relevance to the subject matter? If it is replied that there are moral presuppositions and implications of such a claim, the contention cannot be denied. But why deny it? There is nothing subjective about the claim that killing is morally undesirable; it follows immediately from the human desire to live and the defining axiom of morality—the equality of rights. If someone argues that a murderer has broken this moral rule and hence forfeited his own right to life, he must show how this piece of homeopathic naïveté is to be supported, a task at which his predecessors have labored unflaggingly and failed unfailingly for some millennia.

These moral issues appear again and again in the social sciences. We cannot assess forms of government adequately without commenting on the extent to which they arrange, tend, or neglect to preserve the basic freedoms. Why do we consider such matters? Not just because our culture happens to value them. Our culture happens to value baseball and TV soap opera, but we do not regard concern for these as an appropriate standard to apply to a real-value judgment of another type of government. It is because there are excellent practical grounds for regarding these freedoms as necessary for (or conducive to) the facilitation of the general welfare, whatever the particular tastes of the people. Hence *moral* considerations determine our choice of criteria for comparison between governments, ideal and actual. The arid escapism of the so-called "empirical" school of political science produces pristine but pointless evaluations, with crucial criteria omitted or present but unexplained. It's easier, but it's scientifically incompetent.

Similar points can be made about the process of psychotherapy, where the criteria for improvement or well-being *must* include reference to the way in which the patient treats others, such as his family, subordinates, peers, and superiors. This is not just because unfavorable reactions from them may otherwise lead to a deterioration of his own welfare, but because moral obligations on the therapist require that he take account of the welfare of those who are affected by his patient's behavior. His professional task, in short—not his extra-professional role as a citizen—requires that he be concerned with moral criteria of behavior. He *is* an executive—and an applied behavioral scientist.

It is sometimes thought that if the therapist had restricted his criteria to the present and future well-being of the patient, he would have avoided moral considerations. But this supposition would be true only if the morality of behavior were wholly divorced from considerations of the welfare of those who manifest it—that is, if it were cut off from the most obvious and in fact the only workable rational basis for morality. One can avoid appealing to moral considerations as such, but one cannot avoid recommending, condoning, or criticizing behavior that is moral or immoral.

It is a crucial feature of morality that it involves a commitment to discharge one's obligations even when selfish ends will not be served by such action. But it is a logical slip to suppose that this implies that the moral attitude is not the optimal solution to the problem of maximizing personal welfare. The slip is a subtle one, but fatal. The case for morality rests on the fact that the unselfish attitude provides sources of rewards that are not available to the selfish man, and are more easily available and enduring than those which the latter requires.* It follows that considerations of the welfare of a particular individual (the patient) can rationally lead to the recommendation that he adopt a less selfish attitude, that is, a more moral attitude. So the therapist is *not* avoiding considerations of morality if he makes a truly thorough examination of the forms of behavior available to his patient and bases his recommendation on the patient's welfare, for there is an asymptotic convergence between this and morality. (Indeed he, perhaps more than any other behavioral scientist, *provides* the empirical foundation for morality.) The gap widens with the nearness of death, the extent and stability of the power of the patient, and the rigidity and profundity of his selfishness. For an omnipotent and wholly evil Devil there would be no chink for the rational wedge to introduce moral considerations.

It is always the case, however, for the reason previously mentioned, that the therapist himself must apply moral criteria to the assessment of his patient's condition, since they are relevant. As an applied behavioral scientist, in his particular field, he has no option. One may intellectually distinguish medical ethics from medicine, but one cannot *justify* disregard of one in the practice of the other. In particular, one cannot exclude defensible moral criteria from the judgment of the patient's social-psychiatric condition on the grounds that they are "not scientific." There is nothing scientific about insomnia or psychosomatic dermatitis; they are simply undesirable conditions, and that is

* See "Morality" in *Primary Philosophy* (New York: McGraw-Hill, 1966).

precisely the status of sociopathic behavior. The moment a patient whose behavior can seriously affect other people begins an interaction with a therapist he has entered a situation on which moral considerations bear, and for a practitioner to ignore them is as unrealistic as ignoring the fact that a pregnancy is due to incest or rape when considering abortion. It is not merely a question of bringing in the welfare of others *currently* affected by the practitioner's behavior, but also that of those who *will* be —the spouse of the patient, the unwanted and resented child. Morality requires that their welfare be considered equally with the patient's, and good practice requires that the future inter- actions with them be taken into account in selecting a course of treatment for the patient.

In the design of new schools or new curricula, in the adoption of new teaching techniques or arrangements for student govern- ment and discipline, we find the same necessity for the fusion of moral and non-moral criteria into the overall estimate of the merits of a proposal or a practice. And there is no difference in the role the moral criteria play, nor in the way they are estab- lished (whether as those held, or as those that should be held), nor in the extent to which they are "imposed from without," that significantly distinguishes them from considerations of cost or availability or reliability or performance.

CONCLUSION

So there are good and bad arguments for value conclusions as well as for theoretical conclusions. Whether or not these par- ticular arguments are accepted is unimportant. The challenge to the value-allergic social scientist is straightforward: either *show* that every such argument is unsound or accept the incorpora- tion of their sound conclusions *in* the social sciences. For the arguments are based on facts from the social sciences and on logic —and on nothing else. The purpose of this essay has been to suggest that none of the traditional *a priori* arguments provide an escape from this conclusion.

17 THE JUSTIFICATION OF INDUCTION

Max Black

If a dog barks at me each time I pass by, I naturally expect him to bark again the next time he sees me. This is an example of *inductive reasoning* in its most primitive form. From knowledge about a *sample* of cases, those in which the dog has already barked, I draw a conclusion about a case not included in that sample—I anticipate what will happen the next time.

Let us now take a more sophisticated example: On applying a lighted match to a scrap of cellophane, I find that it catches fire; I conclude that any similar piece of cellophane would also burn in a similar situation. Here we have an inference from what happened in *one case* to what would happen in *any* similar case. One last example: An entomologist finds that each examined beetle of a certain species has a green spot on its back and concludes that *all* beetles of that species will have the same marking.

Such familiar examples of inductive reasoning involve a transition from information about a given set of objects or situations to a conclusion about some wider, more inclusive, set. We might say that all of them consist of reasoning from *samples*. Let us therefore agree to understand by an inductive argument one in which the conclusion refers to at least one thing that is not referred to by the premises.

The simplest forms of inductive arguments, on whose correctness the more sophisticated ones ultimately depend, can be represented as follows: "Such and such *A*'s are *B*; therefore another *A* is *B*" or, again, "*Some A*'s (selected in such and such a fashion) are *B*; therefore all *A*'s are *B*." We need not consider ways of improving these formulas, since the problem of justifying induction remains essentially the same in all forms of inductive reasoning, whether primitive or sophisticated.

It has been held, very widely though not universally, that the use of inductive reasoning is a distinctive feature of scientific method, integrally connected with the discovery of scientific laws and generalizations. In strict *deductive* reasoning, we are limited to rearranging information about the data referred to in the premises, and never advance to knowledge about the hitherto unobserved; by means of inductive reasoning, however, we make the leap from "some" to "all"; from the known present to the predicted future; from the finite data of observation to laws covering all that will be and could be. The so-called "inductive leap" (from "some" to "any" and "all") seems indispensable in science no less than in ordinary life.

Indeed, the very language we use to refer to persons and material objects implies a belief in the permanence of objects and the continuity of their properties that can be grounded only in inductive reasoning from experience. There can be no serious question of human beings rejecting inductive reasoning as unsound: to do so would be tantamount to destroying the very language we use to talk about the universe and about ourselves and would lead to the kind of last-ditch skepticism that lacks even the words to express itself.

It is altogether reasonable to wonder how the use of this powerful method of reasoning can be justified. Indeed, certain features of inductive argument, as we have defined it, can easily awaken serious disquiet. In logic, we have all been taught that the transition from a "some" in the premises to an "all" in the conclusion is a transparent fallacy: if some men are white-skinned, it by no means follows that *all* men are; how, then, can we be justified in wholesale violation of this plain and simple rule? Again, inductions are notoriously fallible; the gambler who expects a sequence of reds on the roulette wheel to continue indefinitely will soon be undeceived. In our dealings with nature, are we in any stronger position than the gambler who has had a lucky sequence of throws? Are we perhaps about to come to the end of our lucky guesses about nature? How can we possibly *know* that the sun will rise tomorrow?

For the sake of clarity, it is essential to distinguish such sweeping skeptical doubts from practical questions about the reliability of inductive procedures. It is one thing to ask whether a given inductive procedure is sufficiently reliable for a given purpose; different and more basic questions are at issue when we ask how *any* inductive argument can be justified. We have well-tested methods for discriminating random events, such as those that occur on a roulette table, from lawful ones: where practical decision is in question, it would be foolish to consider the contingency that the sun might *not* rise the next day. On the other hand, in cases where inductive conclusions based upon sampling are relatively unreliable, we know in principle how to improve the reliability of the sampling process. There is no difficulty in principle about meeting any practical criticism of a given inductive procedure.

By contrast, the question of justification raised by the philosopher is one of the utmost generality. He is perplexed to understand how *any* inductive reasoning, no matter how satisfactory by the standards of common sense or of good statistical practice, can really count as acceptable. He finds it hard to understand how the "inductive leap," which seems to involve a plain logical fallacy, could *ever* be justified. The problem has no immediate bearing upon scientific practice, but is of the first importance for evaluating the claims of science to be a vehicle of truth about the universe. It seems that unless induction can be justified, our claims to have scientific *knowledge* must be rejected as unfounded and science will have to count as no better than any other unsubstantiated *faith*. However appealing such a skeptical conclusion might be to those who welcome any proof of man's impotence, it is one to be accepted only after the most careful investigation.

In the course of the intensive consideration that philosophers of science have given to this problem, almost every conceivable answer has been defended.

1. Perhaps the most drastic solution available consists of a denial that induction plays, or ought to play, any part in scientific method. This view has been most eloquently defended in

recent times by Professor Karl Popper, who has argued in numerous writings that the proper business of science is the *deductive testing* of empirical hypotheses. According to him, there is no rational way of arriving at generalizations from the examination of sampled cases—no rational way of making the inductive leap —but once such a generalization has been produced, by whatever means, there *is* a rational way of discovering whether it meets the tests of observation and experiment. Such generalizations or hypotheses can be conclusively *falsified,* but never verified, never shown to be true. The task of empirical science is falsification, putting to the trial of experience bold "conjectures" about the world, and not the impossible task of discovering truth.

For all the ingenuity with which this provocative view has been argued (to which I cannot do justice in this brief essay), the "no induction" view, as it might be called, has not received wide acceptance. It seems too paradoxical a conception of science that it should consist only of the elimination of error, rather than the progressive discovery of approximations to the truth. And induction seems to creep in by the back door in Popper's theory of "corroboration," that is, of the criteria by which we discriminate between the relative strengths of hypotheses, none of which are falsified by the known observational facts.

2. One might think that common sense can provide a simple and satisfactory answer to the problem of induction. If a layman is asked why he trusts an inductive argument from "some" to "all," the chances are he will say that this kind of argument has "always worked in the past." (One might have some doubts about that "always," but no matter.) How foolish it would be, we can imagine the plain man saying, to abandon techniques that have worked so well and have produced such spectacular successes in technology and in pure science. Well, let it be granted that induction *has* "worked" in the past; what grounds does this give us for expecting it to work in the future? If we conclude that induction *will* work because it *has* worked we are arguing—inductively!

As the philosopher David Hume pointed out long ago in a famous discussion of the problem, we seem here to be begging the question. The best method we have for settling specific empirical questions—arguing from the known character of observed instances—leaves us in the lurch when we try to find a *general* justification of induction. To offer an inductive justification to anybody who doubts that induction is *ever* justified is obviously futile. (On the other hand, some modern writers have argued, with some success, that inductive arguments can be applied to themselves, in order to improve their own reliability. It is at any rate not obvious that any objectionable circularity is here involved. The status of such so-called "self-supporting" inductive arguments is still controversial. In any case, self-supporting arguments, even if allowed to be sound, have no direct bearing on the general problem of justification.)

3. A favorite approach to the problem of justification begins by asserting that inductive arguments, in the form considered in this essay, are basically *incomplete*. Transition from "some" to "all," from a premise about a sample to a conclusion about the population from which that sample was drawn, is held to rely upon unstated *assumptions*. Until such assumptions are made explicit, the inductive inference is unsound—the inductive *leap* is never justified by itself: an inductive argument needs an extra premise in order to become valid. There needs to be supplied some principle that "the future will resemble the past" or some more general principle of "the Uniformity of Nature." Once such a principle has been introduced into the argument, and only then, that argument will become logically respectable. (It will be noticed that this line of attack on the problem tacitly assumes that only *deductive* argument is irreproachable. By implicitly denying the possibility of distinctive inductive arguments, this position resembles the "no induction" view previously mentioned.)

The formulation of general principles that might plausibly play the part of missing premises in inductive arguments is a matter of great difficulty. Since nature obviously exhibits variety as well as uniformity, irregularity as well as order, it is hard to state a principle of uniformity without producing something that is plainly false. For example, the principle that *whenever* some A's are B, all A's are B is a grotesque overstatement. And even such a sophisticated version as John Maynard Keynes's famous principle of the "Limitation of Independent Variety" has been subjected to damaging criticism. It seems fair to say that nobody has yet produced a suitably qualified candidate for the title of the "Basic Principle of Inductive Inference"—although many have tried.

We need not enter into the technicalities of this attempt to bolster induction by supplying an additional grand premise. There is in my opinion a conclusive objection against this whole line of approach. Imagine the desired general principle produced: then it will be either *a priori* true or contingently true. If the first, it is a necessary truth, holding independently of the facts, like a logical or mathematical principle. But then it cannot support the transition from "some" to "all." It is easy to see that if the conclusion of an inductive argument does not *follow* deductively from the premises, the case is not altered when a necessary truth is added to the premises. But if the proposed principle is contingently true, it would not hold in all possible worlds, but must formulate something true of *our* universe.

How then is *its* truth to be known? Only, it seems, by the familiar methods, the best we know, of observation and inductive reasoning. Indeed, we may go further: our confidence in particular laws of nature, the conclusions of inductive inferences, is *better* grounded than our confidence in the truth of any alleged principle about the general uniformity of nature. Such evidence as we have for the orderliness of the universe is derived from our knowledge of particular regularities and not vice versa. The search for grand principles of induction therefore merely shifts the problem without solving it: the problem of establishing such principles is just the old one of justifying induction—in another and even less tractable form.

4. So far, I have made no reference to probability, in order to avoid complicating what is already a sufficiently complicated subject. Yet problems of induction and of probability are intertwined. It is important to notice, for instance, that the conclusion of a sound inductive argument follows from its premises only with a certain probability. Given a good inductive argument for some conclusion, we can always conceive of *stronger* evidence: inductive inferences can sometimes be compared with respect to

their relative strengths in a way that would be quite inappropriate for deductive inferences. Some students of the theory of induction have therefore held that a reference to probability should be part of the conclusion of a properly expressed inductive argument. For instance, the correct conclusion from the premise "All examined A's have been B," they say, is not "All A's are B," but perhaps "It is more probable than not that all A's are B" or something similar. And the suggestion has often been made that neglect of such reference to probability is responsible for the inadequacy of the attempts to justify induction that we have so far considered.

Replacing a conclusion of the form "All A's are B" by a conclusion of the form "It is more probable than not that all A's are B" amounts to weakening the conclusion. (We may recall here that those who hope to add an extra premise concerning the uniformity of nature were engaged in strengthening the premises. So both lines of attack aim at bringing inductive arguments closer to satisfying the standards of valid deductive argument.)

Our verdict on this attempt to make induction respectable by introducing probability must depend upon the meaning we attach to the relevant probability statement. According to one conception of the meaning of probability, the conclusion "It is more probable than not that all A's are B" follows *strictly* from the premise "All examined A's have been B": it is logically impossible that the premise should be true while the probability conclusion is false. On this interpretation, we would have a valid deductive argument, with no "inductive leap," if we introduced reference to probability into the conclusion. But this reading of inductive arguments is useless: our whole attempt has been to understand how it is possible to end in a conclusion that goes beyond the premises, by referring to things or situations that are not covered by those premises. Replacing the original inductive argument by some deductive substitute, however ingeniously constructed, will not be a solution.

There is another way of understanding probability, according to which the probability conclusion makes a genuinely empirical claim about what would be found true in a large number of similar cases. To say that the conclusion is "It is more probable than not that all A's are B" would be tantamount to saying something like "In most cases in which the examined A's have been B, it will be found subsequently that all A's are B." On this view, the argument, as amended by explicit reference to probability, remains genuinely inductive. But by the same token we are confronted once again with the inductive leap. The new conclusion does not follow strictly from the premises, and we are still faced with the troublesome problem of how it can be rational to go beyond the evidence, in the manner that is characteristic of genuinely inductive arguments.

Those who insist that the conclusions of inductive arguments should be probability statements are faced with the same dilemma that bedevils all previous attempts to justify induction: either the argument is left in its original form, and then it seems to be invalid; or else it is replaced by some valid deductive argument (either by strengthening the premises or by weakening the conclusion), and then it is not an inductive argument at all.

5. I turn, finally, to the so-called "pragmatic" justifications of induction, which have seemed to many modern students of the problem to provide a satisfactory answer to this ancient puzzle. The basic ideas underlying this approach were independently formulated by Charles Sanders Peirce and by Hans Reichenbach, the latter of whom argued the position with great ingenuity and pertinacity.

Consider the following familiar position in ordinary life. A doctor, who is treating a patient suffering from some serious disease, has reason to believe that the only chance of saving the patient's life is to perform a certain operation; suppose also that there is no guarantee of the operation's proving successful: if the doctor is right in thinking that the patient will die in any case if the operation is not performed, he is justified in operating. To put the matter in another way: If a *necessary condition* for saving the patient's life is performing the operation, then that operation is justified, even though the outcome is unknown and the risks are great. This might be called a case of "nothing to lose by trying"—resort to the dangerous operation may be a "forlorn hope," but it is a justifiable one.

Those who apply this idea to the justification of induction

argue as follows: Hume was right when he said that it was impossible to argue from the present to the future, from the known to the unknown. The "inductive leap" cannot be justified in the way that philosophers and scientists have hoped. Nevertheless, we badly need knowledge ranging beyond our observations and nothing can prevent us from trying to obtain it. Suppose it could be shown that the *only way* to reach such knowledge is by following inductive procedures. Then we should be in the position of the doctor or the patient in the original example, with nothing to lose by trying. If following inductive procedures is a *necessary condition* for anticipating the unknown, we shall be practically or—as people say, "pragmatically"—justified in following that procedure.

We may agree that the general line of argument is plausible; its contribution to the problem of justifying induction will depend upon how successful its defenders are in showing that some kind of inductive procedure is a necessary condition for making correct generalizations about the unknown or the unobserved.

The model usually employed has approximately the following character: Suppose we are performing a series of observations and are interested in some property P. If in the first 100 trials we find that P has appeared in 65 cases, we assume provisionally that in the *long run* the proportion of favorable cases will be close to $65/100$. As we continue our trials, we may find, say, 87 favorable cases in the first 150 observations: we therefore correct our estimate and now expect the proportion of favorable cases to be near $85/150$. We proceed in this same way: whenever we find that k out of l trials exhibit the property P, we provisionally assume that the proportion in the long run will be close to k/l.

Since there is no guarantee that the fractions we progressively find in this way will ultimately converge to a limit, our attempt to anticipate the overall character of the entire series of observations may be defeated after all. But *if* there is a limit (which we cannot know) this procedure of successive correction will eventually bring us close to the true value of that limit. We are justified in following the procedure, because we have nothing to lose. If the series of successive fractions is sufficiently irregular, *no* method of forecasting its ultimate character will be possible;

while if it has the regularity of a convergent series, our method will bring us close to the desired answer sooner or later.

This idea is too ingenious and too complicated to be criticized in a few words. I have argued at length elsewhere that it fails. Some of the strongest objections that I and other critics have brought to light are technical ones, having to do with the impossibility, according to the pragmatic view, of preferring one method of estimation to another. But the basic objection is that the whole approach concedes too much to the skeptical critics of induction. Those who agree with Hume that *knowledge* of the unobserved is, strictly speaking, impossible, will always find themselves with empty hands at the conclusion of an inductive procedure, no matter how ingeniously they try to wriggle out of their predicament.

We seem now to have arrived at a stalemate. None of the ways of justifying induction that have been explored by a long line of able and acute thinkers seem to offer any prospects of success. Attempts to justify induction by using inductive procedures seem hopelessly circular; attempts to find principles expressing the alleged uniformity of nature simply raise the old questions in a new form; introducing probability statements does not help; and the fashionable "pragmatic" justifications really leave us helpless against skeptical objections to induction. Considering the intensity with which the problem has been studied, there is no hope that we shall do better where so many powerful intellects have labored in vain.

Now when we meet with a situation like this, there is usually reason to suppose that the nature of the problem has been misconceived, and that the apparently insurmountable difficulties arise from misunderstanding. The view is steadily gaining ground that this is the situation with regard to the celebrated problem of justifying induction.

The very notion of justification implies some *standard* of justification: to justify induction must be to show that that kind of reasoning satisfies some relevant criterion of what is regarded as reasonable. Now the long history of the subject shows that nearly everybody who has grappled with the problem has really had before his mind the standards of *deductive* reasoning: however widely the various attempts to justify induction differ, they all assume that the only really reputable mode of reasoning, the only "strict" method, is that in which the conclusion follows by logical necessity from the premises.

But induction, *by definition,* is not deduction: the idea of the so-called "inductive leap" is built into our conception of an inductive argument. To try to convert inductive arguments into deductive ones is as futile an attempt as that of the child who argued that a horse was really a cow—only without horns. The beginning of wisdom in this extremely complicated and controversial domain is therefore the recognition that no *general* justification of induction, of the sort that philosophers of science have hoped to uncover, is either possible or needed. What we *mean* by justifying a specific empirical generalization is an inductive demonstration, using principles that have been found to work in the kind of case in question, that the generalization is true or at least probable. When we try to apply this relatively definite notion of justification to induction itself, the very notion of justification becomes unclear.

It is not so much that we do not know how to justify induction as that we do not know and cannot imagine what we would *accept* as such a justification. Clarity, here—which cannot, of course, be achieved without the hardest intellectual labor—ought to result in the disappearance of the alleged "problem of induction." If this view is correct, as I hold it to be, the problem of induction will eventually be classified with such famous "insoluble" problems as that of squaring the circle or that of inventing perpetual-motion machines. And as in those famous cases, the quest for the impossible does not seem, from the long perspective of history, to have been futile. For the byproducts of serious investigation may be even more important than its ostensible goal. If our knowledge of the character of inductive procedures is as rich and as sophisticated as it is today, no little of the credit must be assigned to those who have labored so long and so unsuccessfully at trying to justify induction.

Index